ARMAMENT AND TECHNOLOGY

AIRCRAFT CARRIERS
SUBMARINES
AND CRUISERS

WITHDRAWN

EX LIBRIS

SOUTH ORANGE
PUBLIC LIBRARY

623.8
Air

To my wife, for all the help she has given me.

Illustrations: Lluis Adell I Jaumandreu, Camil Busquets, Douglas A. Cromby, Octavio Diéz Camara, Jorge Flethes Serrano, Santiago García Gaya, Hanny & Leo Van Ginderen, Jon Godsell, Antonio Moreno Garcia, Marc Piché, Diego Quevedo Carmona, Chris Sattler, Harry M. Steele, Vicente Talón, Ralph Thorsteinson, Winter & Findler, Leonid Yakutin, Aerospatiale, Alenia, Alstom, the Spanish Navy, "Bazán" National Company, Daniel Bechennec, Blohm + Voss, Bofors/Celsius, Celsius/Kockums, Centre IMP/Helio DCN Cherbourg, Colebrand Defence, DCN International, Denel LIW/Vektor, Eurosam, Fincantieri, GEC Alsthom, GEIE Eurotorp, GE Marine & Industrial Engines, Jeumont Industrie, Kollmorgen/GE, Konsberg, Litton Ingalls, Lockheed Martin, Marina Mlitare, Marine Nationale, Matra Bae Dynamics, McDonnel Douglas, Meval, Nordic Defence Industries A/S, Oerlikon-Contraves, Studio Grafico Restani, the Royal Navy, STN Atlas Elektronik, Swedish Navy, Thomson Marconi, US Navy, Voith Hydro.

Researcher: Albert Campanera I Rovira

Computer specialists: José Manuel Rojo Ara and Albert Rojo Mateu

Production: Ediciones Lema, S.L.
Editor: Josep M. Parramón Homs
Text: Camil Busquets
Co-ordination: Eduardo Hernández

© Ediciones Lema, S.L. 1999

I.S.B.N. 84-95323-12-5

Photocomposition and photomechanics: Novasis, S.A.L.
Barcelona (Spain)
Printed in Spain

ARMAMENT AND TECHNOLOGY

AIRCRAFT CARRIERS
SUBMARINES
AND CRUISERS

LEMA
Publications

Conventional aircraft carriers, which operate with jet planes taking off with the aid of a steam catapult and then being retrieved with the aid of a cable arrest systems across the deck, will experience many changes in the future.

French Aircraft Carriers

France was in the forefront of naval aviation remembering Clement Ader and his aircraft, eventhough their experience of wheeled aircraft taking off from aircraft carriers came later than the Americans (at the end of 1910 the American pilot "Ely" took off from a wooden deck installed on the fo'c'sle of the light cruiser *Birmingham*. On the 18th of January 1911 the same pilot continued his exploits from a similar ship, but this time using the after deck of the heavy cruiser *Pennsylvania*). Later, on the 8th of May 1914, the pilot Caudron took off from the ocean liner *Foudre*.

Despite this, France did not have a true aircraft carrier until 1926 when the Bearn entered service, a Normandy class battleship which was converted as a result of the 1922 Washington Treaty. During the Second World War occupied France could not finish the two aircraft carriers *Joffre* and *Painleve*, these having been under construction since 1938. For this reason the first French carriers to be designed and completely constructed in France were the *Clemenceau* and *Foch*, two

THE CHARLES DE GAULLE

The nuclear aircraft carrier *Charles de Gaulle* that we can see in this picture some months after its launch, will be the most important surface ship to be constructed in France's history. It is smaller than the large American CVNs, but incorporates well proven features.

excellent aircraft carriers. As these ships were designed and built in the mid nineteen fifties they are now coming to the end of their life span

The Charles de Gaulle

On the 23rd of September 1980 the French Defence Council agreed to construct two nuclear powered aircraft carriers to replace, first the *Clemenceau* in 1996, and the *Foch* some years later. The construction order for the first, with the name of *Charles de Gaulle*, went out on the 4th of February 1986. The first section was put in placed on the 14th of April 1989 and she was launched on the 7th of May 1994.

She is expected to enter service in December 1999. The other ship, which may be

THE DRY DOCK

We can see the *Charles de Gaulle* from the bow in the dry dock receiving its finishing touches.

called *Richelieu*, or as has been more recently suggested *Clemenceau*, still does not have a clear future due to budget cutbacks. If its construction is finally authorized it is unlikely to be in service before 2004 or maybe not even for some years after that.

With a fully loaded displacement of 39,680 tons, the ship will be powered by two PWR K15 reactors and two GEC Alsthom turbines producing a total of 83,000 horsepower being put through two propellers.

The hangar with dimensions of 138.5 x 29.4 x 6.1m will house 20 to 25 aircraft. It will have a runway angled at 8.5 degrees and two 19 x 12.5 m lifts each with a lifting capacity of 36 tons to lift the air wing on to the 261.5 x 64.4

STARBOARD ELEVATORS

This ship has a particular characteristic, wich is the arrangement of the two starboard lifts. These are positioned behind the island, which is supposed to protect it from the water and large waves. It is one of the few aircraft carriers which has all its lifts, arranged on one side.

m flight deck. This group will consist of the new *Rafale* and the older Super Etendards, Hawkeyes and Panther helicopters.

The *Charles de Gaulle* will be able to operate continually for five years without the need to refuel its nuclear reactor. Its reactors generate steam for all its on board services including the two catapults which are able to launch aircraft of up to 22 tons in weight.

One special characteristic of this ship is that its lifts are arranged projecting out on the starboard side, located behind the island in such a way that they are protected if it is ever necessary for them to be operating in bad weather.

Its armament consists of four VLS modules with eight launchers with the new SAM Aster 15 missiles; two Matra Sadral PDMS modules with six launchers and eight 20mm GIAT 20F2 guns with a rate of fire of 720 rounds per minute. A complete set of equipment with sensors of every kind including ESM/ECM components will make up its array of electronic systems.

The crew will consist of 1,950 men (1,150 for the ship, 550 for the air group and 50 general staff), this includes space for a further 200 should the need arise. The ship is also equipped to carry a battalion of 800 marines.

THE CV-77

An artist's impression of how the CV-77 could be. Its appearance will be very different to existing aircraft carriers.

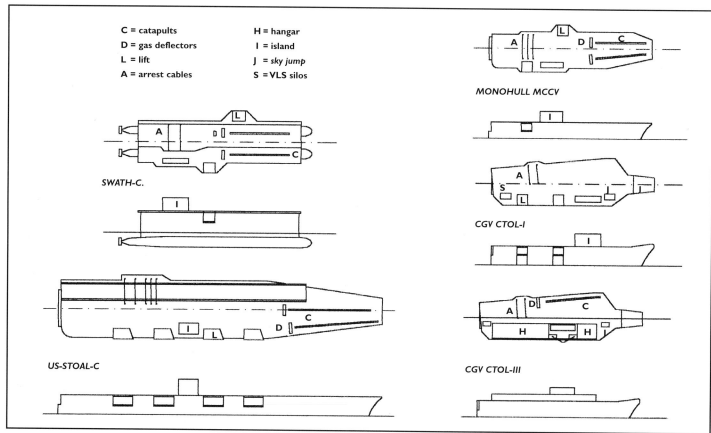

C = catapults
D = gas deflectors
L = lift
A = arrest cables

H = hangar
I = island
J = sky jump
S = VLS silos

SWATH-C.

US-STOAL-C

MONOHULL MCCV

CGV CTOL-I

CGV CTOL-III

From the CV-77 to the future North American CVX

A new ship is expected to be added to the Nimitz class, which will probably be very different from all the others.

The CV-77

Little is known about this ship although it will be authorized in the 1999 financial year, with construction beginning around the year 2002. Because of the statements made with regards to its characteristics it seems that it will have the same propulsion plant as the Nimitz class, even though its external appearance will be very different. Substantial changes are expected for the island that is if it has a structure, which can be, given such a name. The same applies to many other services and details. Its dimensions and displacement will be very similar to Nimitz class ships.

Future CVX Aircraft Carriers

Everything about the ships, which are due to replace the existing conventionally powered CVA's, continue to be the source of much speculation. There is nothing definite in this respect and alternative designs are being considered, with a variety of projects and research

THE PROJECTS
In this illustration we can see different projects for future US Navy aircraft carriers.

work being undertaken.

At least six distinct projects exist, amongst which can be found enormous aircraft carriers of 214,000 tons to other mini versions of only 26,500 tons. In addition there are references to the so-called floating island or Mobile Offshore Base (MOB), an idea advocated by Admiral William A. Owens, in his time the US Navy's second in command. This island would be formed by six interconnected modules, which would have an estimated displacement of 500,000 tons. It would not have its own propulsion system and would instead be towed to flash points around the world wherever they may be. It would operate with an air wing of 150 to 300 aircraft of every type, and amongst these it would have to include the likes of the Hercules C-130 transport aircraft. In the following sections we will describe the other projects which are known of.

Ultra Large STOAL (Short Take off Arrested Landing) Concept

These are an extension of the Nimitz class, incorporating nuclear propulsion and with dimensions expected to be in the region of 465 m in length and a beam of more than 50m at the waterline. These aircraft carriers will have a flight

deck of a similar length and a width of some 85 metres. The flight deck is not angled and parallel to it is a section equipped with 5 arrest cables with two catapults in the bow, each one with jet exhaust deflectors. The expected air wing is between 120 and 140 aircraft, with 5 lifts (4 on the starboard side and one on the port side, the actual position still undefined).

SWATH Minimun Capability CV Concept

The SWATH (Small Water Area Twin Hull) configuration is a project that is likely to receive the go ahead. It will be used by the US Navy for its ocean surveillance ships, such as the T-AGOS 19 Victorious, and offers the specific advantages of many of the smaller carriers in use today.

It would have a displacement of 84,000 tons,

CHARLES DE GAULLE
Once launched it was towed to the fitting out berth to be finished while afloat. The elevator positions are significant, both on the same side, a detail which can be perfectly appreciated in this photograph.

THE CONSTRUCTION
The Charles de Gaulle can be seen along its starboard side during the construction stage in September 1998.

a length of 239 m and beam of 50 m. The flight deck, including launching areas and overhangs would measure 250 x 67 m, with a maximum distance of 92 m between both of the lifts. With reference to the underwater section of the hull, this would include the facility for launching two large torpedos, 3 m long by 0.13m diameter.

It would be powered by electric motors, probably with cryogenic cooling. The aircraft complement will be around 30 aircraft, with two catapults and two lifts, one on each side of the hull. The island with dimensions of 34 x 8 m at its base, would be located on the starboard side. The same as the UL/STOAL Concept, it would have a hangar deck, only in this case located between both hulls.

Other projects

Another four projects were considered in addition to those already mentioned: the Monohull Minimum Capability Concept (conventional type aircraft carriers, smaller than the Nimitz); the CGV-CTOL (Version I) Concept (a ship similar to the Russian Admiral Kusnetzov type cruiser-aircraft carriers); the CGV-CTOL (Version III) Concept similar to the earlier mentioned craft, except without a hanger deck; the CGV-STOVL Concept (A modernised Invincible, with sky-jump, which would operate with STOVL aircraft).

COMPARISONS OF ORIGINAL CHARACTERISTICS: CHARLES DE GAULLE, CV-77 & PROJECTS

CLASS	YEAR DELIVERED.	DIMENSIONS.	DISPLAC.	BOILERS	ENGINES	POWER	SPEED/RANGE	WEAPONRY
Ch. de Gaulle CV-77	1999	238 x 31.5 x 8.5	40,550	K-15 PWR Reactors	2 GEC Alstom Turbines 4 Westinghouse Turbines	76,000 280,000	27-nuclear 35-1 million	VLS (4xVIII) EUROSAM Aster 15 CIWS Matra Sadral (2xVI), 20mm Giat 20F2 guns (8x1) RAM/Phalanx CIWS, Stinger,etc. 80 aircraft.
CV-77	2008	333 x 41 x11.9	102,000	PWR (2) A4W Westinhouse Reactors	Turbines	350,000	35-NC	120-140 Aircraft. No missiles
UL/STOAL	2020 approx.	465 x 50 x NC	214,000	Nuclear	Electric engine	NC	30-NC	30 No missiles
SWATH	2020 approx.	239 x 50 x NC	84,000	Electric/cryogenic	Electric engine	NC	30-NC	14 VLS 192 cells
Monohull	2020 approx.	235 x 37 x NC	47,000	Electric/cryogenic	Electric engine	NC	30-NC	12 VLS 192 cells
CGV (I)	2020 approx.	235 x 33 x NC	35,800	Electric/cryogenic	Electric engine	NC	30-NC	14 a 22 VLS 64-192 cells

VLS MODULE

The Charles de Gaulle will employ four modules each with eight EUROSAM vertical launchers, which will include amongst others the new Aster 15 missile.

MISSILE LAUNCHERS

These Sadral defense missile launchers are used as a counter measure against sea skimmer missiles in the last phase of their flight, with an altitude not less than 3 m, a range of up to 4 km and a 3 kg warhead.

NUCLEAR FUEL

This is a fusion element (normally enriched uranium) which produces a large amount of heat, regulated by a graphite moderator. The heat produced increases the temperature of water contained in the primary circuit, hermetically sealed and isolated from the outside.

CHARLES DE GAULLE

The aircraft carrier *Charles de Gaulle* in construction at the Brest Naval Dockyard, two months after being launched.

SAGAIE DECOY LAUNCHERS

Used for launching all kinds of decoys, it is specially designed to give passive self-protection to surface ships. It can fire up to 10 decoys.

NUCLEAR PROPULSION

The primary circuit acts as a heat exchanger with the water contained in the secondary circuit. This water, converted into steam, directly drives the propulsion turbines. Nuclear propulsion is only different from the conventional way in its use of a particular type of fuel.

ALTERNATOR-MOTOR

This is basically equipment, which is powered by a diesel engine. The engine drives the alternator, which produces electrical power at the appropriate voltage, amperage and frequency.

Towards the end of the 1970's the British began to put together a project for a somewhat novel type of ship, which practically speaking was more of an amphibious ship without the landing craft, and significantly less than an aircraft carrier. From the beginning it was classified as a "Through Deck Cruiser".

In reality these are medium sized ships with a flight deck and hangar, with some capability for carrying troops and a departure point for assault helicopters and the transportation of equipment. Its main role is foreseen as the control ship in amphibious operations. With the availability of STOVL aircraft, which until then had been V/STOL, these aircraft carriers became the first of a new type of carrier which went on to become the first carriers to install and use a bow ramp to assist the aircraft taking off. Having perfected the take off from the bow ramp or *ski-jump* they were capable of operating with STOVL aircraft in addition to helicopters.

The Falklands War caught the British off guard, almost without aircraft carriers (the status of the *Hermes* has already been mentioned), and with only one of the Invincible class carriers in commission and the landing ships H.M.S. *Fearless* and H.M.S. *Intrepid* in reserve. The Royal Navy still managed to enforce the exclusion zone around the Falkland Islands, and to land and protect the liberating forces.

The Invincible class ships displace 20,600 tons when fully loaded, and are powered by 4 Rolls Royce Olympus TM-3B gas turbines, in a COGAG system and two propellers. Its maximum speed is 28 knots, with a range of 7,000 miles at 19 knots. Its air wing consists of British Aerospace FA2 Sea Harriers, Westland Sea King & Merlin EH-101 helicopters.

The classic aircraft carrier provided with take off catapults, an angled flight deck and arrester cables is an expensive and complex ship. For this reason there are very few navies which have them. The most common are those which operate only with STOVL aircraft and helicopters.

The Invincible Class

Since the 1970s when H.M.S. Ark Royal, H.M.S. Eagle and H.M.S. Victorious were retired from service, Great Britain abandoned having conventional aircraft carriers in the Royal Navy. In fact the only conventional type aircraft carrier which participated in the Falklands War was the *H.M.S. Hermes*, a ship which was laid down during the Second World War and which was extensively modernised on three occasions. She operated with STOVL aircraft and at the time of the Falklands was on the point of being transferred to India. This eventually occurred, in 1986 after she had gone through an exhaustive refit at Devonport dockyard. She was then renamed *Viraat*.

ARK ROYAL

The third vessel of the Invincible Class is H.M.S. *Ark Royal*, which can be easily identified by being the only one of the three which uses the American Vulcan Phalanx CIWS guns instead of the Dutch Goalkeeper.

MARCONI RADAR

At each end of the island these ships have Marconi 909 firing control radar's located inside the dome housings. Above the bridge is the Marconi Signal Type 1022 search radar, with a range of 265 km.

GIUSEPPE GARIBALDI

The *Guiseppe Garibaldi* has a ramp at the bow with an angle of only 6.5 °, which although good enough for operation, does not have the same effectiveness as those with a steeper angle. The Navy has plans for a very different vessel, which will probably be very similar to the Spanish *"Principe de Asturias"*.

The armament, in addition to its own air wing, is made up of SAM Sea Dart missiles (36 missiles) in a double launcher at the bow. These are being removed as the ships enter their refits.

Three CIWS Goalkeeper or Vulcan Phalanx mounts, depending on the ship, and two 20mm Oerlikon/BMARC guns. It is considered that the armament of these ships is their weak point, and that they should carry more weapons if their size is taken into account.

With respect to the electronic systems these consist of the Marconi Signal type 1022 for

HANGAR

These ships have a hangar type which does not extend from one side of the hull to the other, with the result that it is narrower and smaller than is normally found with aircraft carriers, resulting in a less favorable aircraft to displacement ton ratio.

air search, the 992 R or Plessey 996 for surface search and the Kelvin Hughes 1006 or 1007 for navigation. Firing control is carried out by the Marconi 909 or 909(I) radar. The combat system is not uniform across the three ships. They are also fitted with ESM/ECM counter measure decoy launchers.

Its crew is made up 685 men (60 officers), to which another 366 (80 officers) from the air wing must be added. Up to 600 marines can also be carried when necessary.

Of the three ships only two are permanently operational, the third being kept in reserve, undergoing refit and modernization.

The Giuseppe Garibaldi

Up to the 29th of January 1989 the Italian Navy was held back by the heavy burden of obsolete and outdated legislation dating back to the years of Italo Balbo and Mussolini, which in practice restricted having any kind of fixed wing aircraft.

Nevertheless, from the 1970's Italy equipped its Navy with cruisers provided with flight decks at the stern, operating only with anti-submarine type helicopters. NATO leaders assigned this role to the Italian fleet during the cold war when facing a powerful enemy Soviet submarine fleet.

As a result, the construction of a cruiser with a flight deck was ordered on the 21st of November (similar in appearance to the British Invincible class). However, it can only be considered as a ship with a helicopter air wing - V/STOL aircraft at that moment did not seem possible.

Nevertheless this ship, even when it was virtually a contemporary of the Invincible class, has significant differences to them with a smaller displacement, an offensive capability which is lacking in the others though the defense capability is similar. She has no amphibious capability; neither does she have any accommodation for troops or marines. With respect to the ramp in the bow, which is so important

CIC

The CIC is located in the *Garibaldi's* large island, the most important function on present day warships, a place somewhat exposed for missile attacks.

THE INVINCIBLE

The Invincible is the first of the series. During its inaugural journey to Australia she suffered serious engine breakdowns and had to be repaired in India. In January 1989 she began a refit that lasted for 27 months, during which, the angle of the ramp in the bow was increased from 5 degrees to 12 degrees.

in these kinds of ships, it has a smaller angle (only 6.5 degrees compared with the normal 12), reducing the performance of its aircraft.

The *Garibaldi* is a 13,850 ton ship at full load, propelled by four LM-2500 gas turbines in a COGAG configuration with two propellers. Its maximum speed is 30 knots, with a range of 7,000 miles at 20 knots.

Her armament is the most powerful to be found in this type of ship, with the exception of the Russian versions. This confirms that the project was undertaken at a time when the ideas associated with it were not very clear. At present she is fitted with four OTO-Melara Teseo Mk-2 anti-ship SSM missiles; two SAM Aspide missile mounts with eight launchers (48 missiles in total including reserves); six 40/70 mm Breda guns (3 x 11) and two mounts with three 324 mm ASW torpedo launchers.

Curiously, its identification on the side of the hull continues to be that of a cruiser, C-551, in comparison with the British Invincible class which have always carried the "R" for aircraft carriers.

Its aircraft wing is made up of a maximum of 16 Harrier II STOVL AV-8B aircraft or 18

SH-3D Sea King helicopters, although it is normally a mixture of both. It is important to highlight that the first Italian V/STOL Harriers were not operating from this ship until December 1994, a difference of 12 years when compared with the Spanish, British and Americans.

The *Viraat,* ex *Hermes*

Until the arrival of the *Chakri Naruebet* in the Thai fleet, India was the only country of the then so-called third world, which had an aircraft carrier. As such it was a symbol of the military power held by the so-called largest democracy on the planet.

WEAPONRY

These ships (the Ark Royal is in the picture) were criticized for their modest weaponry which consists only of a twin SAM Sea Dart launcher, which will be removed as they undergo refits, three CIWS mounts and a couple of 20 mm GAM B01 Oerlikon guns.

LIFTS

In this aerial photograph of the *Garibaldi* the position of the two lifts on the deck can be appreciated, one situated at the bow and the other at the stern of the island.

Construction began on this ship in 1944 and was completed at the end of 1959. Meanwhile it formed a part of the Royal Navy, where it was subjected to major modernization work on three occasions and then a fourth when it was sold to India. Its incorporation into the Indian fleet enabled the Indian Navy for a short time at least, to operate two carriers, the *Vikrant* (the ex *Hecules*), having been commissioned into the Indian Navy in 1961, was a smaller ship which had also been supplied by Great Britain.

With the work carried out in 1986-1987 the Viraat received new fire control equipment, as well as navigation radar, improved take off features, and improvements to the NBC (Nuclear/Biological/Chemical) warfare systems. In 1995 it received new radar equipment, while at the same time off-loading its obsolete Seacat missile system, replacing them for Gatling AK-230 guns along with 40 mm anti-aircraft guns.

It has a capacity for up to 30 STOVL aircraft, although normally it doesn't operate with more than 12, along with SH-3 ASW/ASV/Vertrep & Ka-27 helicopters. It also has four disembarkation LCVP's at its disposal.

There are plans for some new modernization work in the coming years, to be carried out in the Indian dockyards of Mazagon in Bombay.

A COMPARISON OF THE CHARACTERISTICS

	INVINCIBLE	G. GARIBALDI	VIRAAT
YEAR DELIVERED	1980	1985	1959
DIMENSIONS	209 x 27.5 x 8	180 x 33 x 6.7	227 x 27 x 8.7
DISPLACEMENT	20,600	13,850	28,700
PROPULSION	COGAC/gas turbine	COGAC/gas turbine	4 Admiralty boilers
ENGINES	4 Rolls Royce TM3B	4 Fiat/GE LM 2500	2 Parsons
POWER	97,200	81,000	76,000
SPEED/RANGE	28-7,000/19	30-7,000/20	28-NC
WEAPONRY	- Sea Harrier/Plus STOVL aircraft (12) - Merlin EH-101 Sea King helicopters (12) - SAM Sea Dart missiles (1 x II) - CIWS Goalkeeper guns (3 x VII) - 20 mm Oerlikon guns GAM-B01 (2 x I)	- AV-8B Harrier II STOVL aircraft (8) - SH-3D Sea King helicopters (8) - Mk2 SSM Teseo missiles (4 x I) - SAM Aspide missiles (2 x VIII). - 40/70 Breda guns (3 x II) - Mk46 ASW Torpedos (2 x III)	- Sea Harrier STOVL aircraft (12) - Sea King & Ka-27 Helix helicopters (7) - 40/60 Bofors (2 x I)

RADAR

The RTN 30X is used to guide the Aspide missiles. It is a monopulse radar which operates in the L waveband (between 8 and 10 Ghz). The *Garibaldi* is fitted with three outfits.

SAM ASPIDE MISSILES

SAM Aspide missiles have a semi-active radar tracking warhead, with a range of up to 13 km at Mach 2.5 and is effective from 15 up to 5,000 meters altitude. The Garibaldi has a total of 48 missiles, six complete loads for each launcher.

NETTUNO SLQ-732

The ESM/ECM electronic warfare equipment used by the *Garibaldi* is the Nettuno SLQ-732, which provides wide coverage against enemy radar detection.

TORPEDO LAUNCH TUBES

The *Garibaldi* is also armed with two 324mm torpedo launch mounts with three tubes each. These use the Mk-46 ASW torpedo which is being replaced by the new A-290.

ANTI-SHIP MISSILES

The *Garibaldi* is the only aircraft carrier in NATO to carry SSM anti-ship missiles, which are the Mk2 OTO Melara Teseo. This is a sub-sonic missile (0.9 Mach) with a r ange of 180 km and which will be substituted soon by the Mk3, with greater range (300 km) and bigger payload (160 compared with 210 kg).

GUNS

A part of the anti-aircraft and anti-missile system is covered by the three 40/70mm double Breda mounts. Each gun has a rate of fire of up to 300 rounds per minute, with a range of 12.5 km against ships and 4 for anti-aircraft/anti-missile use.

The large attack aircraft carriers in service with the US Navy at the moment are the direct consequence of the constant growth of weight, size and features of the aircraft on board.

A long development

During the Second World War the aircraft carrier superseded the battleship as the glamorous ship of the combat fleets, relegating it to the role of a mere escort in some instances. Though as such, the battleship did have a very important role during the allied landings, when their large bore guns supported the troops on the ground, a role that has also been put to good use in recent years as well.

During the Korean War the flight decks on a lot of carriers had to be reinforced. Because of the full operational use of jet engined air-

THE LIFTS

The American CVN's have four lifts with a capacity of 58,500 kg each for transferring aircraft from the hangar to the flight deck. In this picture one of these can be seen in its bottom position, as well as two others located on the deck forward of the island.

THE *HARRY S. TRUMAN*

The latest CVN to join the US Navy is the U.S.S. *Harry S. Truman*, CVN-75, delivered in July 1998. This ship was going to be called the United States, but negotiations between the two large political parties meant that its name had to be changed.

craft which were much heavier than propeller driven airplanes angled flight decks were fitted at the same time to facilitate the take off of jets. This was due to the peculiarities of the propulsion system with the direct intake being dangerous on the flight deck. This had not been a problem until then.

The constant improvements made to the jet engine with the corresponding increase in the aircraft's weight and the need for longer landing/takeoff area brought about the need for a larger type of aircraft carrier. This became a reality with the appearance of enormous, for the period, James V. Forrestal class, later succeeded by four Kitty Hawk class vessels. The most obvious external difference between them being the more rational layout of the four lifts.

In 1961 the *Enterprise* entered service, the first nuclear powered aircraft carrier. This ship was used as a test case for evaluating this new propulsion system; its undoubted advantages were demonstrated against other conventional aircraft carriers. These included its greater range as well as the greater supply possibilities it offered its air wing.

These nine ships (4 Forrestal, 4 Kitty Hawks and 1 Enterprise) carried out invaluable service during the Vietnam War (1964-1975) during which its air wings played a role in tens of thousands of missions.

Meanwhile the principal behind the Enterprise project, was proven when, in 1964 when work began on a nuclear super aircraft carrier project. The first was the U.S.S Nimitz, which entered service in 1975, too late to have participated in the Vietnam War. Ten similar ships have been or are being constructed based on this vessel, the last two of which will enter service in 2002 and 2008.

A minimum number

The US Navy considers that to carry out its obligations at an optimum level it is necessary to have between 12 and 15 attack aircraft carriers. These together with its corresponding Task Forces or Operation Groups

---

THE ISLAND

An aircraft carrier's island is not only a point from which to control the ship (which mustn't be confused with the CIC or Combat Information Centre), but is also the base for a multitude of detection sensors, communication and electronic warfare (EW) equipment.

THE *AMÉRICA*

The American fleet of large nuclear submarines has to be complemented by an adequate number of ships with conventional propulsion, such as the *America* CVA-66 in the photograph. This is to enable it to reach a total which meets the objective of maintaining operational the number of task forces specified for the various fleets (Pacific, Atlantic etc).

---

constitute the backbone of the forces, which the USA has used in many of the crisis in recent times. But now with the number of nuclear aircraft carriers only at 9, including the Enterprise, it has to continue maintaining a number of conventional vessels in service from the Forrestal and Kitty Hawk classes.

Because of the length of time these ships have been in service which in some case is quite considerable. This moves away from what is considered to be the maximum operational life of a warship ship, usually between 20 and 25 years. Of the 13 aircraft carriers the US Navy has at this moment, 54% of these, seven ships, are more than 20 years old.

Named after great men.

Traditionally, American aircraft carriers are named after battles that took place in the United States or where the United States has intervened. This system was changed with the Forrestal class, which in addition to the lead ship "James V Forrestal" (who was a Navy secretary), also saw the names of Politicians, John F. Kennedy for example, mixed with others from a variety of different kinds of backgrounds.

With the Nimitz class only the names of famous political and historical celebrities have been used, resulting in negotiations between the two large parties the Republicans and Democrats. With respect to the last two ships U.S.S. *Harry S. Truman* and U.S.S. *Ronald Reagan*, the name Truman was only conceded

A COMPARISON OF THE CHARACTERISTICS

CLASS/QTY	YEAR DELIVERED	DIMENSIONS	DISPL.	BOILERS	ENGINES	POWER	SPEED/RANGE	WEAPONRY
Forrestal (4)	1955/1959	317 x 39 x 11.3	79,000	Babcock (8)	Westinghouse Turbines (4)	260,000	34-12,000/20	4 x 127 mm (I) 100 aircraft
Kitty Hawk	1961/1968	330 x 39 x 11.3	79,000	Foster Wheeler (8)	Westinghouse Turbines (4)	280,000	35-12,000/20	4 SAM Terrier II (2) 100 aircraft
Enterprise (1)	1961	336 x 40 x 11.3	86,100	Westinghouse Reactors PWR (8) A4W	Westinghouse Turbines (4)	280,000	35-297,000	Not provided 100 aircraft
Nimitz (9)	1975/2002	333 x 41 x 11.3	99,050	Westinghouse Reactors PWR (2) A4W	Westinghouse Turbines (4)	280,000	35-1 million	3 x Sea Sparrow (VIII) Mk 29 3 x Phalanx CIWS (VI) Mk 16 80 aircraft
CV-77	2008	333 x 41 x 11.9	102,000	Westinghouse Reactors PWR (2) A4W	Westinghouse Turbines (4)	280,000	35-1 million	RAM/Phalanx CIWS, Stinger, etc. 80 aircraft

if the last of the series was to be called Reagan.

True Leviathans

The large Nimitz and Enterprise class nuclear aircraft carriers, as well as those which have survived from the Forrestal and Kitty Hawk classes, are spectacular and enormous ships in every aspect. They are in a select group of ships, which are more than a 1,000 feet in length, this length being something of a watershed in ship design.

Construction on angled slipways was abandoned with these ships, as much as for the weight to be moved (some 60,000 tons) as for their size, which make a slipway launch impossible. As a result they have been constructed in dry docks of which the dimensions are even more spectacular, with a 400 x 100m

THE AIR WING

The air wing of an aircraft carrier consists of 80 different types of aircraft. In this view we can see the deck of the *George Washington*, CVN-73 with approximately half of its complement of aircraft. There are F-14 Tomcats, F-18 Hornets, EA-GB Prowlers, E-2C Hawkeye's, S-3B Viking, ES-3A Shadows and SH-60 Seahawk anti-submarine helicopters.

surface area and a depth of 30m. The height of one of these ships is equivalent to a 24 story building.

The displacement of a Nimitz at full load touches 100,000 tons in the first ships (*Chester W. Nimitz; Dwight D. Eisenhower; Carl Vinson & Theodore Roosevelt*), this being surpassed in the later five (*Abraham Lincoln; George Washington; John C. Stennis* and the already mentioned *Harry S. Truman* and *Ronald Reagan*).

Everything on these ships can be described as enormous, with a flight deck measuring 333m in length and 77m maximum width. They have a surface area equivalent to three football fields, the deck also has to withstand a weight of 30 tons each time one the aircraft lands on it at speeds of 300 km/hour.

Its complete air wing is made up of nearly

THE MOST POWERFUL

A nuclear attack aircraft carrier is the most powerful surface ship to have ever sailed the Oceans. Although its main weapon is its air wing it is also equipped with defensive weaponry: three banks of SAM Sea Sparrow missile launchers, CIWS multi-barrelled Vulcan Phalanx guns and anti-torpedo decoys.

80 aircraft of all types, including some helicopters. The principal power source is two General Electric A4W/A1G pressurized water PWR nuclear reactors, with enough fuel to sail for more than a million miles. The reactors produce steam for the four sets of turbines, which produce 260,000 horsepower and give the ship a maximum speed in excess of 30 knots (some 55 km/h) and a range limited only by its requirements for provisions, munitions and supplies. The crew consists of 6,000 men and women, with nearly 600 of these being officers (3,184 for the ship, 2,800 air wing and 70 general staff).

The construction and fitting out of this ship, including the mounting of a variety of equipment (but without counting the design or manufacture time) accounted for something in the order of 40 million man hours.

Nuclear aircraft carriers really are floating cities where all the necessary services can be found. On board these monsters there are 3,400 internal spaces for accommodation (offices, cabins, compartments etc), all with air conditioning. The cable network on board is so extensive that it would measure, with the cables put end to end, more than 1,500 kilo-

RADAR PROTECTION

Radar emissions can effect the human organism, especially at short distances. To avoid such effects special screens are placed at the appropriate points. This view shows the island of the *Theodore Roosevelt* CVN-71 with its protection from, amongst other things, the AN-SPS-49(V)5 aerial search radar.

meters. In parallel there are more than 30,000 lighting panels or lighting points as well as 2,000 telephones. The potable water equipment daily treats some 2 million liters-2,000 m3, enough for 2,000 houses.

The galley on board prepares 18,000 meals every day. The total number of manuals required for the ship's different systems to function, one on top of the other, would form a column

Weaponry

Although an aircraft carrier's weaponry consists mainly of its aircraft, they possess a combined destructive capacity equivalent to that of all the United States forces during the Second World War. There are also other weapons systems on board these ships self defense: CIWS anti-missile multi-barrelled Vulcan Phalanx guns and SAM Sea Sparrow & RAM missiles. Its electronic sensor equipment is proportional, with aerial and surface search radars. It also has ESM/ECM electronic warfare systems made up of interceptors and disrupters, numerous decoys to confuse enemy sensors both in missiles and torpedoes.

Although the type of aircraft carrier air wing depends particularly on the mission to be carried out, in general it is a mixture of fighters, bombers, supply planes, surveillance and electronic warfare, etc.

higher than the highest building in Spain (170 m), and the 6,250 mattresses, put end to end, would reach more than 12 km. The size of one of these ships is such that to get an idea of how big they are, consider that if two crew members wanted to have a drink together (which have to be non alcoholic, the US Navy doesn't allow alcohol on board warships) then they would have to arrange it well beforehand bearing in mind that months could pass without them seeing each other.

Lastly, the electricity production capacity could satisfy, without any problems, the needs of a city with 100,000 habitants.

THE FLIGHT DECK
The large size of a CVN flight deck is patently clear in this image. The maximum width is some 77m, and 38 m at the stern.

AN ADAPTED DESIGN
The lifts are designed to meet the needs of loading and carrying aircraft and with the objective of fitting two on each trip. From there they are adapted to the appropriate form, depending on the kind of aircraft operating on board these ships.

Those ships considered to be lightweight aircraft carriers consist of two subdivisions. One part consists of those ships described as through deck cruisers, up to a point a kind of hybrid, and the other part being those truly lightweight squadron aircraft carriers for limited air operations, ships which can be considered as a hull with a hangar and flight deck.

The *Príncipe de Asturias*

This ship could be considered as one of the best managed and well defined projects of the many modern aircraft carriers constructed, although in some aspects she could have been improved.

The origin of this ship goes back to the 1970s when the American admiral Elmo Zumwalt, head of the US Navy's operations put forward his idea of what the future Sea Control Ship (SCS) should be like, based on a ship design philosophy with a limited cost. The Gibbs & Cox design office carried out pre-project work on how this new ship was going to be. In the background was the idea of the SCS being a multi-purpose ship with a wide range of features, carrying out both limited air operations and also working as a command ship for merchant navy convoys, especially the tanker fleets. But this was always under the

AIR WING

Although at the time of the photograph the Chakri did not have its air wing, it is in fact made up of 6 AV-8S STOVL Matadors (Harriers) and some S-70B7 helicopters. In addition its deck is adequately reinforced to operate with twin rotor Chinook helicopters.

premise that it would be a cheap ship, with massive construction programs being foreseen for the inevitable war with the Soviet Union. In this war the battle of the Atlantic of the past would be a child's game compared with what was going to happen.

But the US Navy threw this project out as a result of International events, as well as the necessities deriving from that which pointed the way more towards two particular types of ships: large attack aircraft carriers and amphibious assault ships.

As a consequence of this, at the end of that decade, the Spanish Navy had to think about the replacement of its old and worn out *Dedalo* and began considering specific possibilities. The US Navy abandoned the project later, though with the approval of the design company, the state company Bazán (involved in

COMMAND BRIDGE

This is a part view of the Command Bridge of the Principe De Asturias. The ship's Captain, or on occasions the officer in charge of manoeuvres, gives the orders relating to the sailing of the ship from the seat which can be seen in the background. On the monitors each and every item of information necessary for controlling the ship is displayed.

THE FORWARD ANTENNA

The *Principe de Asturias* is constantly being modernized, the latest modifications on board being the incorporation of a satellite communication system with improved levels of performance. We can see in this shot the corresponding antenna, located at the front of the bridge island

naval construction work) bought the plans.

Although it may sound strange, what Bazán actually received was not more than a dozen drawings, which had to be completely developed and increased to more than the 4,000 necessary to construct the ship. That is why it must be considered as genuinely Spanish,

CHAKRI NARUEBET

We can see the *Chakri Naruebet* during one of its sea trials before being delivered. The shape of the hull for both this ship and the *Principe de Asturias* has been so successful that they can continue operating in sea conditions, in which other ships of a similar size would find difficult.

although at the same time respecting its undeniable American origins.

An outstanding ship

The *Principe de Asturias* is an aircraft carrier with a hanger stretching from one side of the ship to the other, in other words it takes up the whole of the ships beam. This is something that differentiates it from other Through Deck Cruisers where the hanger doesn't normally occupy more than a part of the beam. In addition the Hanger extends close to two thirds of the total length of the ship, with the bow section reserved for flight services and living quarters. At the same time the two lifts are located in areas different to the other cruisers mentioned, one positioned at the stern, just at the end of the flight deck and the other in front of the island, using this system allows the hanger to function without.

It is a ship which has repeatedly surprised those who have seen it operating in rough seas and which has been kept in operation when others ships were unable to do so. This is a result of its lateral stability, controlled by means of two sets of computer controlled stabilising fins. At the same time, thanks to the 12 degree sky-jump at the bow the ship is able to continue launching and receiving aircraft even in force 5

MULTIPURPOSE CAPABILITY

The *Principe de Asturias* has become the archetype of how a lightweight squadron aircraft carrier should be. It is a ship with multipurpose capability, which allows it to carry out a wide range of different operations. At the same time, with its capability as a command ship, it makes up the nucleus of its fleet.

gales (heavy seas with waves of up to 4 metres high), as long as the pitching doesn't exceed 12.

Propulsion and maneuverability

When dealing with a ship with a limited budget it is logical that some of the costliest parts are modified and included from the outset of the project. Falling into this category is the single propulsion shaft with a five bladed propeller. The propeller has variable pitch, the blades being hydraulically controlled, which results in a diameter that varies between 6 & 10 meters. It weighs 35 tons and in its time was the biggest of

BRIDGE ISLAND

On the *Principe de Asturias* the island has different important features, in particular the Primary Flight Section. In practice this is the control tower for all of the surrounding air space, an overhanging cabin located at the foot of the mast. This mast is a latticework construction supporting all of the electronic sensors.

its type in the world. The propeller is connected through a hollow shaft to the gearbox unit, which has a reduction ratio of 1:24. This shaft is 45 meters in length and weighs 174 tons, and contains 2 tons of grease. Its maximum rotation speed is 150 rpm. The hydraulic system controlling the propeller works at a pressure of 70 kg/cm^2 in normal operation and 112 kg/cm^2 during maneuvers.

A possible problem would be if the ship was left without propulsion following a break down or enemy attack, but this can be overcome by the use of two auxiliary propulsion units (APU's). These offer a lateral movement, which also gives excellent additional turning capability for docking maneuvers. These systems are retractable so that they do not cause resistance when the ship is under way. They are made up of a Kort nozzle and propeller directly driven by an electric motor.

The main engines are two LM2500 General Electric gas turbines, which drive the propeller though a reduction gearbox. She is also fitted with a single semi-compensating rudder.

A powerful Air Wing

The *Principe de Asturias* has a wide operational area, in practice the largest of all the ships in its class, even exceeding those of other larger ships. As such, her maximum operational capacity is 27 aircraft, which increases to 37 for

SIGNIFICANT SIMILARITIES

The similarities between the aircraft carriers *Principe de Asturias* (Spain) and the *Chakri Naruebet* (Thailand) are quite striking. These follow a series of logical developments with the first constructed from an existing design base (with some tidying up) and the second a later development of this.

transport missions, although this depends on the type of airplane being dealt with.

In general the aircraft on board are the STOVL AV-8B Harrier II / Harrier Plus and a variety of helicopters: SH-3D/G Sea King, SH-3D Sea King AEW, AB-212 EW and SH-60B Sea Hawk. The number of each type is variable depending on the operation to be carried out.

Anti-missile Weapons

The *Principe de Asturias* has four defense points using twelve 20 mm MEROKA multi-

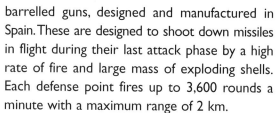

SIMILARITIES

The range of the *Principe de Asturias* is such that it can sail for 6,500 miles at a speed of 20 knots. This is the same as going from Spain to the United States and back, although if necessary it can also be refueled at sea. In the photograph we can see a maneuver of this type involving the fleet tanker the *Marques de la Ensenada*.

barrelled guns, designed and manufactured in Spain. These are designed to shoot down missiles in flight during their last attack phase by a high rate of fire and large mass of exploding shells. Each defense point fires up to 3,600 rounds a minute with a maximum range of 2 km.

The Chakri Naruebet

When the Thai Royal Navy thought about providing itself with a lightweight aircraft carrier in the 1970s, it seemed at first that it would go for a vessel of German design and construction. In the mid 1970s the supply of this ship to the Thai navy was put out to open bid following an earlier open bid process which had been tainted with irregularities.

Nearly all of the important dockyards in the world were involved in the open bid, but the one which finally won the contract was the Spanish State Company Bazan, which offered a ship based on its *Principe de Asturias*, although adapted to meet the conditions of the contract.

In the history of aircraft carrier construction this was the first to be ordered by one country and then built in another. It has demonstrated that it is an outstanding ship based on an excellent design. It has produced

admiration in many who have seen it sailing or who have sailed on board it. At the moment it is the last ship of its class to be constructed.

Based on the *Principe de Asturias*, it is a smaller vessel although its longest launch way covers practically the whole length of the flight deck. The layout of this part of the ship is similar.

The propulsion system is a twin and mixed unit. It is a CODOG system with two diesel engine/gas turbine plants, without the auxiliary propulsion units. Each one of these engine groups consists of a General Electric LM 2500 gas turbine and a MTU 16V 1163 TB 83 diesel engine and drives a variable pitch propeller.

The standard of crew accommodation is similar to the *Principe de Asturias*, but with fewer places (600 men). However, there is one unusual aspect in that a VIP suite (for the Thai royal family) has been included high up on the island, this is able to accommodate four people.

The weaponry is different to that of the Spanish ship, because of the need to have homogenous units across the whole of the Thai fleet. As a result of this it has been fitted out with a vertical launcher with eight cells for launching SAM Sea Sparrow missiles; three Sadral missile launchers with a capacity of six missiles; four 20 mm CIWS Vulcan Phalanx mounts and two 30 mm guns. Some parts of the weaponry just mentioned have still not

12 DEGREE SKY JUMP

Here the flight deck of the Principe de Asturias is shown from the highest point of the sky-jump (angled at 12 degrees). With this ramp the STOVL aircraft take off by being catapulted into the sky, increasing its weapon carrying capability and range. This is due to the fact that taking off in this manner uses much less fuel than doing so vertically.

been fitted onto the ship, but it is expected that this will be done in the near future.

Its air wing consists of STOVL AV-8S Harrier aircraft in addition to SH-70 B7 helicopters. In addition it has been prepared to operate with heavy helicopters such as the Chinook.

The latest news about this class of aircraft carrier is that there will probably be a third LPD to be constructed for the Spanish navy. It will be an amalgamation of the Chakri and the Galicia design with two thirds of the bow section similar to the first and the last third similar to the second.

It will have a sky jump for operation with STOVL aircraft and a helicopter deck. The internal hold and stern door will give it characteristics suitable for amphibious missions.

This new ship will be an excellent substitute for the *Principe de Asturias* on the occasions when she is undergoing refit or is on other operational duties.

COMPARISION OF CHARACTERISTICS

SHIP	P. DE ASTURIAS	C. NARUEBET
YEAR DELIVERED	1988	1997
DIMENSIONS	196 x 24 x 9.4	183 x 22 x 6.2
DISPLACEMENT	17,188	11,485
BOILERS	Gas turbines	CODOG
ENGINES	LM 2500 (2)	LM 2500 (2)
POWER	46,400	44,250
SPEED/RANGE	25-6,500/20	26-10,000/12
WEAPONRY	Meroka CIWS (4 x XII)	VLS (1xVIII) with Sea Sparrow missiles
ENGINES		MTU 1163 (2)
POWER		11,780
WEAPONRY		Matra Sadral (2 x VI) Vulcan Phalanx (4 x VI) Guns 30 mm (2 x 1)

The incorporation of aircraft carriers in the Soviet fleet has been a relatively recent event, so much so that these ships have suffered deeply from the changes in the political regime in this part of the world.

A hazy history

In 1939, in accordance with the third five year plan (1938-1942), Stalin cancelled the construction of two aircraft carriers. These were going to be called the *Voroschilov* and *Lyetl*. The cancellation seemed to have a lot to do with the pledge on the part of the Germans to transfer the plans of the *Graf Zeppelin*, which was being built by Deutsche Werke shipyards in Kiel and which was launched on the 8th of December 1938.

> **THE LAUNCH RAMP**
> In this photograph taken in Malta in the 1990s the considerable length of the launch ramp can be appreciated. It is nearly 25 meters long and with a sky jump angle of 12 degrees.

> **AN ISLAND PACKED WITH ELECTRONICS**
> The Kusnetzov's island contains the greater part of its electronic equipment. In this part view from the port/bow side of the ship we can see clearly the Sky Watch 3D panels as well as two Cross Swords for the SAM's on each side, with one of the two Strut Pairs high on the bridge. It is also possible to see the SATCOM radar antenna.

In those years relations between Germany and the Soviet Union were going though something of a difficult time, the height of which was in 1940 with the sale of the hull for the heavy cruiser *Lutzow*, the fifth in the Blucher class. This also included the sale of a number of 381/47mm naval guns and several other important weapons. Only the hull of the *Lutzow* was delivered, before Germany invaded Russia in June 1941.

The Moskwa

Russia emerged after the end of the second world war as one of the strongest powers in the world. At the end of the 1950s, early 1960s, found itself with the problem of having to prepare itself for a possible large scale naval war, but with its technology at a level which was not suitably developed to do so. The fighting which established the USSR as a major power during the second world war was predominantly ground based, with the maritime aspects being left in the hands of its allies, the Americans and British. As a result, they were left with the considerable challenge of constantly having to think about how they could carry out a naval war on a large scale against the two most powerful navies in the world.

At the beginning of the 1970s the powerful US Navy had at its disposition the first six attack aircraft carriers of the Forrestal, Saratoga and Kitty Hawk class, plus the nuclear carrier U.S.S. *Enterprise*. In addition there were also the new SSN's and the dangerous SSBN's.

The first were excellent auxiliary ships in the aircraft carrier fleets and the second a fearsome and new strategic weapon which left a large number of Russian cities within the reach of their nuclear missiles.

The incipient Soviet fleet could only oppose all of this with large numbers of outdated, obsolete ships which still employed technology and strategies more in keeping with the second world war and barely appropriate to face up to modern nuclear submarines.

The solutions which Western Navies came up with for dealing with such submarines were ASW helicopters and helicopter carriers. As a result it was logical that the Russian navy also designed and constructed these types of ships. The Moskva and Leningrad, with flight decks for only carrying helicopters, entered service in 1967 and 1968 respectively.

They were ships with a maximum displacement of 19,200 tons, 190 meters long with steam turbines driving two propellers. They had a maximum speed of 30 knots and a range of 12,000 miles at 15 knots. All of which was along the same lines as Western helicopter carriers.

These ships had a 86 x 34 meter flight deck at the stern, just behind the large bridge, and operated with ASW Ka-25 Hormone A helicopters. These were housed in the hanger below the flight deck, this having a capacity for holding 18 aircraft. Access to the hanger was by two appropriately sized lifts. They were classified as Protivolodochny Kreyser, meaning anti-submarine cruisers.

The Kiev class

These are considered quite clearly to be off-shoots of the Moskva, although they have double

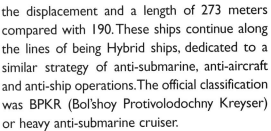

A SAD FATE

The collapse of the Soviet Union has led to unprecedented shortages in the Russian armed forces. The fleet has not been able to avoid these with its ships languishing in a semi-abandoned state in various Russian ports until they are broken up or sunk without further use. In this photograph we can see the Kiev in Murmansk, in August 1993.

WEAPONRY IN THE BOW

On the *Kiev* the weaponry is concentrated in the bow of the ship, in the fo'c'sle. Located in this part of the ship are two ASW RBU 6000 mortars; a twin bank of ASW SUW-N-1 missiles; a twin 76/60mm gun turret; SSM SS-N-12 Sandbox missiles and a twin bank of the SAM SA-N-3B Goblet missiles.

the displacement and a length of 273 meters compared with 190. These ships continue along the lines of being Hybrid ships, dedicated to a similar strategy of anti-submarine, anti-aircraft and anti-ship operations. The official classification was BPKR (Bol'shoy Protivolodochny Kreyser) or heavy anti-submarine cruiser.

At the beginning it was expected that the complete series would be made up of four ships (*Kiev, Minsk, Novorossyisk and Baku*). However, this last one entered service after a construction process which was so modified, that in practice it became a quite different kind of ship. These ships were delivered in 1975, 1978 and 1982.

Fitted with an angled flight decks of 4.5 degrees, but without catapults or arrest cables, these ships could only operate with 12 Yak-38 Forger STOVL aircraft, 18 Ka-25 Hormone A or Ka-27 Helix ASW helicopters and two Ka-25 Hormone B helicopters (for guiding missiles). The forecastle bristles with powerful missile weapon systems based on four twin banks of the SS-N-12 Sandbox, with SAM SA-N-3, 4 and/or 9, depending on the ship. There are also numerous AK-630 CIWS mounts.

These ships have suffered considerably from the shortages effecting the Russian armed forces since the disappearance of the USSR. It is difficult to know exactly what their current operational situation is although it is presumed that they must be in quite a precarious position. A significant number of them have already

been removed from operational duties, but it is still from certain that they will be broken up.

The *Admiral Gorskov*, the ex *Baku*

Around 1974 the General Staff of the Russian navy began to seriously consider the philosophy of having "defensive" aircraft carriers. This meant a large, multipurpose ship acting as the flagship, controlling the fleet, with the capability of carrying out aerial operations. This ship had to be provided with adequate weaponry, of a type which would allow it to successfully confront every type of aerial attack, be it from aircraft or missiles.

A ship's construction from the design phase to commissioning normally takes ten years or more, especially if a large ship like an aircraft carrier is being built. It is because of this, that as soon as the navy got a hold of the fourth ship *Baku*, of the Kiev class, a variety of modifications were incorporated turning her into something of a test bed. It was delivered in 1988, which was a considerable delay on the original forecasted date of 1982.

Essentially, the *Baku* has to be considered the same as her sister ships, even if she does have an island that is radically different. This ship was a test bed for the trials of phase array antenna systems, which later had to be fitted on the

ON DECK MISSILE LAUNCHERS
One of the most peculiar aspects of the *Admiral Kusnetzov* is that it has 12 VLS modules for SSM SS-N-19 Shipwreck missiles installed on the deck just at the beginning of the *sky jump* ramp, at the central gangway.

ON BOARD AIR WING
The *Kusnetzov's* air wing is made up of Sukhoi Su-27 fighter aircraft for its own defense and Su-25s employed for training purposes. The two aircraft shown in this photograph are the *Frogfoot*, in front of the *Flanker.a*

Tblisi and *Riga*. Its official title is AKR (Avionosky Kreyser), aircraft carrier cruiser, indicating a change of mentality with regards to this kind of ship. At the same time it has to be borne in mind that the aircraft carrier concept had never existed before that time in the Russian navy.

Her displacement is slightly greater than the Kiev's, with the dimensions almost the same at 273m long, 32.7m beam when afloat and with a 10m draft instead of 9.5m, she is also equipped with an angled flight deck of 4.5 degrees. However, the armament on the fo'c'sle is more powerful, with the ship having at its disposal twelve instead of eight SSM SS-N-12 Sandbox missile launchers with 24 missiles in a magazine. The total of SAM SA-N-9 Gauntlet missiles in VLS housings is 192, distributed in four batteries, two at the bow and two at the stern, in six modules with eight launchers.

The two 76/60 mm twin gun turrets were substituted by two simple 100/70 mm guns to which were added eight CIWS AK-630 mounts. Two ASW RBU 12000 mortars were also included.

With respect to the electronics aspects, in addition to the previously mentioned phase array antennas, this ship is fitted with the new Fly Trap/Cake Stand radar equipment (housed in the dome) for the control of aircraft.

When the USSR broke up the Baku, the name of the capital city of Azerbaijan, changed its name to the *Admiral Gorshkov*, named after the founder of the modern Russian fleet. As has happened with her three sister ships the likelihood of the *Admiral Gorshkov* continuing in service is doubtful. It seems likely that she will continue to be held in reserve in Rosta, although it is said that India is interested in her possible purchase.

The *Admiral Kusnetzov, ex Tblisi*

This ship is the lead ship of a group which should have also included the Riga, but which could not come to fruition as a result of the chaos and troubles following the break up of the old political regime in Russia. However, as the lead ship she has managed to survive and live something of a charmed life, with the second ship languishing away without any real prospects of ever putting to sea. So much so that it has been offered to China, but without success, being rejected for a series of electronic problems. There have also been some serious thoughts about scrapping it as well, in the meantime it continues to age prematurely.

She has a displacement of 67,500 tons when fully loaded and is 280m long when afloat, with a beam of 37m and a draft of 10.5 m (the flight deck is 304.5 x 70m). This ship is an amalgam of many theories and studies carried out in the Russian Navy in the 1970s and 1980s.

They are aircraft carriers in the truest sense of the word. They are fitted with a generous 12 degrees sky-jump and an angled deck of 7 degrees. They use four arrest cables and deflectors for the exhausts from jet engines, although they do not have any type of catapults which determines what kind of aircraft can normally be used. There are four types: the Sukhoi Su-25 UTG

THE FREEBOARD

The *Kusnetzov's* freeboard is greater than that of the Kievs/Baku, 16 meters against 13. This was because of the need to have lifts at the sides of the ship, which in heavy swells could have made operation difficult.

TAKE OFF DECK

In this photograph the large size of the overhanging take off deck is very clear, something which is very normal in most aircraft carriers, but not normally the case on Russian ships.

Frogfoot; eighteen Su-27K Flanker Ds; fifteen Ka-27 Helix and two Ka-31 AEW helicopters.

The *Tblisi* carried out its sea trials in 1989 and changed its name the following year. The Riga (the capital of Latvia) changed its name to the Varyag.

The *Ulyanovsk*

This ship, which should have been an improvement on the Kusnetzov's, uses nuclear propulsion and steam catapults. It was programmed for delivery in 1996, but at the moment nothing for sure is known about it. Given the difficult circumstances which the Russian Navy is experiencing there is not a great deal of hope for the future of the ship.

AIRCRAFT CARRIER CRUISERS

The *Baku*, the fourth ship in the Kiev class, although modified, can be considered as a ship in its own class. It entered service in 1987. In this photograph we can see it sailing at full speed in 1988.

ELECTRONICS

In this part view of the *Baku's* island from the starboard side we can appreciate the Tin Man optronics systems, in the centre of the picture, and a Cross Sword radar to the right for SAM SA-N-9 missiles.

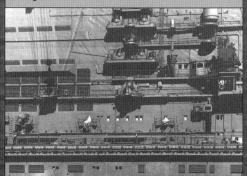

NEW ELECTRONICS

The bridge island has incorporated new phase radars in the form of square, flat panels and corresponding to the three dimensional Sky Watch radar. This is a Russian replica of the American SPY-1 system.

SHIP'S IDENTIFICATION

Russian ships normally use a different type of identification system to that of Western Navies, with numbers which change according to the area in which the ship is operating (for example, the Baltic, Black Sea, Arctic or Pacific). Positioned behind the crane, the two 100/70mm guns and on the stern side of the eight AK-630s, all of the characters appear painted in a dark colour.

BOW LAUNCH AREA

One of the consistent features of the Russian aircraft carrier classes Kiev, Baku & Tblisi is the large launching area at the bow, which is close to 25 meters long. Thanks to this it has incorporated a very long flight deck without increasing the length of the ship. On the fo'c'sle there are 10 barrelled ASW RBU 12000 mortar systems which can fire 80 kg projectiles up to a distance of 12 km.

WEAPONRY AT THE BOW

A variety of weaponry can be found on this ship's fo'c'sle with the SS-N-12 located next to the VLS housings for the SA-N-9 Gauntlet supersonic missiles. Running between each of the SSMs is a small reloading vehicle.

ELECTRONICS

Nearly all of the sensors are located on the Baku's bridge island even though the weapons are positioned in various parts of the ship. In this photograph we can see the stern section of the island showing another Cross Sword radar for the SAM SA-N-9 missiles, which can be found more to the right.

INFLATABLE RAFTS

Inflatable life rafts are present on the ships of every navy in the world. This is especially true for those which have a large number of crew, such as the *Baku* which has some 1,600 men not including those in the Air Wing.

WEAPONRY AND ELECTRONICS

Two CIWS AK-650 mounts are housed at the stern of the ship, on the starboard side, along with an associated Bass Tilt radar. A little further forward twin decoy launchers can be observed on a small platform. They are a type which appeared in the Moskva class in the early years of the 1970s.

BOAT DAVIT

The boat davits on board the *Baku* are similar enough to those used on other ships where the force of gravity and the boats own weight are used to launch them into the water. They also include auxiliary winches.

FLIGHT DECK EXTENSION & BRIDGE ISLAND

This picture shows some of the port side of the ship where the extension of the flight deck at the bow can be appreciated. In addition, half way along the island is the Command Bridge (primarily for flight control) and higher up is the cylindrical Cake Stand radar unit, 8 meters in diameter, used for controlling aircraft.

The concept of the amphibious assault ship is a relatively modern idea. In fact it refers to ships with a flight deck from which troops are transported to landing zones by helicopters, or which use aircraft (kept in a hanger) to provide air support.

Amphibious Assaults

The landing of ground troops with the aim of occupying a country is an action which is nearly as old as mankind itself. We are told

THREE SHIPS IN ONE

An LHD, which in this photograph is the lead ship of the Wasp series (LHD-1), combines in one ship the military power of three. As a result the total number of ships required at the moment by the US Navy is less than would have been used previously.

IFF INTERROGATOR

Taking together the usual type of electronic sensors, the IFF interrogator is one of the most important, allowing the ship to know sufficiently in advance if the contact obtained is a friend or enemy. In this photograph an IFF Mk12 AIMS UP X-29 unit is shown, made up of 64 RF transmitters mounted in the crown (which is 3.75 m in diameter and 0.4 m high).

about many celebrated landings which helped to change the course of history.

However, without doubt the most famous amphibious operations are those which took place this century in the Dardanelles during the first world war and which ended tragically, or in Alhucemas in the African War in 1925. Together with those which were carried out in the Pacific and Normandy during the Second World War.

All of these landings had a common denominator in that troops where carried to beaches in landing craft or barges, disembarking on foot and under enemy fire. Often with a considerable number of casualties.

The Inchon landings during the Korean war signalled a turning point in this type of operation, but it was not until Vietnam that a new kind of vehicle was used on a massive scale, the helicopter. With this a radical change in strategy and amphibious tactics came about, helping to introduce the modern support aircraft that we have today, the first in history to be truly amphibious.

The LPH Iwo Jima

With helicopters now the means of transport in such operations this made it essential that ships were specifically designed to operate with them. During the 1970s the US Navy built a class of ships, the 7 ships in the Iowa Jima class, created for such missions, of which some still survive today. However, before these ships were built a number of aircraft carriers

TWO IWO JIMAS IN ACTIVE SERVICE

Of the seven original Iwo Jima's the US Navy is still operating with two, one of which will soon be taken out of service. The Inchon was re-fitted and is now involved in mine laying/sweeping activities (MCS-12) with specially equipped Sea Stallion helicopters.

were converted into this type of ship to gain experience with the various concepts. They have a flight deck, but without arrester cables or catapults, and have a capacity of some 25 helicopters. These are brought up from the hangar to the flight deck by using two lifts, one on each side of the ship.

The ship has enough space to accommodate up to 2,000 fully equipped marines in addition to its 750crew members. Because of this they need sufficient internal capacity to be able to store 24,000 liters of fuel for their motor vehicles, 1.5

BRITISH AMPHIBIOUS SHIPS

The *Ocean*, seen here in this photograph before she was commissioned, is under going sea trials in April 1998. It is the first amphibious ship built by Great Britain in more than 30 years. The two Vulcan Phalanx mounts on the stern can be seen very well here, on both the overhanging sections. The same applies to the ramp used for loading and unloading vehicles.

million liters of JP-5 for the helicopters, 1,060 m^3 of space for palletised cargo and 400 m^2 of parking space for all types of vehicles.

The propulsion system consists of a steam turbine unit connected to single-shaft and propeller. The weaponry has evolved from the early days, and at the moment consists of two CIWS Vulcan Phalanx guns and 12.7mm & 25 mm Bushmaster machine guns. All of the SAM Sea Sparrow missile units have been removed, as has the 76mm gun, which was originally installed.

The LHA Tarawa

Until the advent of the Wasp class, these ships were considered to be the best ships of their type to have been built to date. At the beginning it was expected that nine ships would be built, but this was reduced to five as a consequence of the budget cuts which followed the end of the Vietnam War.

In one ship of this class there is a combination of the features of a LPH (Iwo Jima), LPD (Austin), LCC (Blue Ridge) and LKA (Charleston). This means that it has the capability of operating as a helicopter carrier while at the same time as being a dock for the disembarkation of marines, a command ship and attack transport. For this it receives the title of LHA / Amphibious Assault Ship, general purpose.

Because of this, she has a large internal hold area (82 x 24 m) from which troops, vehicles,

A COMPARISON OF THE CHARACTERISTICS

CLASS/QTY	YEAR DELIVERED	DIMENSIONS	DISPL.	PROPULSION	ENGINES	POWER	SPEED/RANGE	WEAPONRY
Wasp (7)	1989/2001	257 x 32 x 8.1	40,532	Combustión Engineering/Steam boilers (2)	Westinghouse turbines (2)	70,000	22-9,500/18	Sea Sparrow SAM missiles (2 x VIII) CIWS RAM missiles (2 x XXI). CIWS Vulcan Phalanx (2 or 3 x VI) 12.7 mm machine 1guns (4 u 8 x I)
Tarawa (5)	1976/1980	254 x 32 x 7.9	39,967	Combustión Engineering steam boilers (2)	Westinghouse turbines (2)	70,000	24-10,000/20	CIWS RAM missiles (2 x XXI). CIWS Vulcan Phalanx (2 x VI). 25 mm Mk 242 automatic guns (6 x I) 12,7 mm machine guns (8 x I)
Iwo Jima (7)	1961/1970	188 x 32 x 10	19,600	Combustión Engineering	Westinghouse	23,000	23-10,000/20	CIWS Vulcan Phalanx (2 x VI). 25 mm Mk 38 automatic guns (4 x I) 12,7 mm machine guns (4 u 8 x I).
Ocean	1998	203 x 34 x 6.6	21,758		Diesel engine (2)	23,904	19-8,000/15	CIWS Vulcan Phalanx (3 x VI). Oerlikon/BMARC 30/75 mm (4 x II)

landing craft and VCA/LCAC can be disembarked. There is also a large hanger, 250 x 24 m with a height of 6m, which can be used to transport its air wing. This is made up of CH-46D/E Sea Knight and CH-53D Sea Stallion helicopters as well as STOVL AV-8B airplanes (up to a total of 35 aircraft). These are transferred to the flight deck by using the two lifts, one laterally positioned with a load bearing capacity of 18 tons and another in the stern of 36 tons.

MODIFICATIONS

The Tarawa class have been modified on various occasions throughout their lives especially with respect to their weaponry. In the photograph we can see the head ship of the series in March 1998, with the original 127mm gun emplacements, one on each side of the bow, empty.

The different internal decks are connected to each other by means of cargo lifts (1,000kg capacity) and include ramps for troops and vehicles. Its load capacity comes to more than 1,900 men; 3,134 m² for vehicle parking; 3,311 m³ palletised cargo; 38,000 liters of fuel for vehicles and 378,000 JP-5 fuel for the aircraft. They carry a variety of units for disembarkation with different variations being possible. Some of the varieties are: four LCU's; two LCU's and three LCM-8's; 17 LCM-6's or forty five LVTP-7 amphibious tractors. A variety of internal distribution problems within the cargo hold mean that it can only operate with one LCAC. It also has a large hospital area with three operating theatres and space for 300 beds.

For missions where it acts as the command ship she always sails with the appropriate General Staff on board, as well as an extensive CIC, housed in the island. The positioning is something that has come in for some criticism, because it is in an exposed position and therefore easily hit by SSM missiles.

The LHD Wasp

At the height of the Reagan administration, authorization was given for the construction of seven ships of this class, the last of which will enter service in the year 2001.

The philosophy behind the project is very similar to that of the Tarawa class, even though

there are some differences, which have brought about a change in the name of this type of vessel to a multipurpose LHD/Amphibious Assault ship. It surpasses the Tarawa class in some ways, in particular with respect to dimensions and size, although by a small margin. The main differences, in addition to those already mentioned, consist of the following: distinct positioning of the lifts (one on the port side, the other on the starboard side), both the same with respect to size and load handling capacity; a smaller troop carrying capacity of 1,685 men; small differences in the cargo capacity; the ability of shipping up to three LCAC's; distinct positioning of the CIC (in

the hull, below the hangar deck) leaving it in a location which is better protected; a hospital with a greater capacity (600 beds) & six operating theatres and an island at a lower height as a consequence of the deck being lower. The air wing is slightly bigger with similar types of airplanes and/or helicopters. In addition the new Osprey V-22 has been going through evaluation trials on these ships.

With respect to the propulsion system of both classes of ship the main engines are steam turbines with two propellers. Together with similar weapon systems which have been undergoing changes for as long as they have been in existence. At the moment this consists of Sea Sparrow and RAM missiles (only RAM on the Tarawa class) CIWS Vulcan Phalanx guns, 25mm guns and 12.7mm machine guns.

The HMS Ocean

The British Royal Navy learned its lesson from the Falklands experience by maintaining an amphibious force, which is sufficient for the country's needs. Its latest acquisition is H.M.S. Ocean, a helicopter carrier specially created for modern amphibious operations, and for use as an auxiliary vessel for use in parts of the world, which are prone to natural catastrophes.

LANDING FORCES

The main strength of an LHD or LHA lies in its landing force which is made up of a contingent of nearly 2,000 fully equipped marines, including vehicles which are carried to the land by CH-46 Sea Knight helicopters, as can be seen in the picture above.

LANDING CRAFT

Landing craft, which go into action with air support, are each able to carry a good number of light and medium combat vehicles. Here we can see a LHD packed with vehicles and equipment, containing three LCAC's (photograph to the left).

COMMUNICATIONS

As they also perform amphibious command tasks. LHD/LHA also possess a considerable capacity for communication, and also every kind of search and patrol sensor (right hand photograph)

It is the first helicopter carrier as such constructed in Great Britain, at the same time as being the first amphibious ship delivered to the Royal Navy since the mid 1970s. She was built in two different shipyards with Kvaerner Govan on the Clyde given the responsibility for the hull. Once it was launched she sailed on its own power to the VSEL yard (Vickers Shipbuilding Engineering Ltd) at Barrow in Furness where she was fitted out.

The first news of its construction came in 1987, although from 1989 until May 1993 (when the contract was signed) there was a complete stop put on the project. In May 1994 the first blocks on the slipway were positioned and on the 2nd of October 1995 the ship was launched. She was finally commissioned into the Royal Navy in August 1998. Her hull is based on the same design as the Invincible class, although as a result of the needs of the project its size and dimensions are different. The philosophy behind the project is similar to that of the Invincible class, albeit with inferior weaponry, a lower speed and at the same time reduced features from a military viewpoint.

She is able to operate STOVL aircraft, although she does not have a sky-jump at the bow or possibilities for board on maintenance of the aircraft. Her flight deck has been reinforced to allow her to operate Royal Marine Chinook helicopters in addition to the Navy's Sea King, Merlin and Lynx. From the year 2005 it will also be operating with Apache helicopters.

Her disembarkation abilities, in addition to her helicopters, she is also equipped with four Mk5 landing craft. She does not have an internal loading bay, though two VCA Grifons it will be operating will be launched from retractable ramps at the stern of the ship.

She has a capacity for approximately 830 fully equipped marines, to which can be added 40 vehicles of many different types. She also has two lifts, which link the flight deck with the hangers, as well as a garage at the stern for the disembarkation vehicles. At the moment not much is known about other equipment fitted to the ship.

BRIDGE ISLAND

The LHD/LHA's bridge island is the ship's nerve center where nearly all of the different weapon and sensor systems are controlled. This bridge island from the Wasp class, is bristling with antennas for a variety of different functions, such as the SPS-52C aerial search radar high up on the bridge or the SLQ-32(V)3 electronic war equipment a short distance below it.

LHD

The two LHD's in this photograph are moored in a dock in the Norfolk Naval base, in September 1998, the Keasarge next to another unidentified ship. This ship is not on operational duty, having been immobilised for either maintenance work or leave.

SLBM's, or submarine launched intercontinental-ballistic missiles, are the most terrible and powerful weapons ever created. They are difficult to react against because of their ballistic trajectory and flight altitude, with multiple nuclear warheads, which can destroy many different cities in any corner of the world.

A terrible weapon

The frightening possibilities of this weapon have been known and demonstrated since the launch of the deadly V-2 rocket on London by Nazi Germany. This rocket would arrive in silence and its effect was felt for a long time after it had exploded.

The allied countries took note of what was happening in this area and after the war put the technology to use in their own weapons. As such the USA soon had a non-ballistic missile, the Regulus, an advanced version of the V-1, which in the 1950s was launched from a variety of different ships in its navy, including submarines. Of the latter, two conventional submarines were constructed between 1957 and 1958 (the U.S.S. *Grayback* and the U.S.S. *Growler*), and in 1959 the nuclear U.S.S. *Halibut* was specially built to operate with this missile.

In parallel the V-2 was improved, eventually ending up as the Navy's Polaris missile and the army's *Jupiter,* a weapon that made the first space launches possible. The Polaris program was begun in 1955, although different activities had been taking place associated with it, but without any name, since 1952.

The first firing of a Polaris under water took place in 1961 from the nuclear submarine U.S.S. *George Washington*, the head of the series. A variety of later improvements led to the creation of the *Poseidon* (1971) and the *Trident* (1981), whose most powerful version, the C-5, was put into service at the end of the 1980s and beginning of the 1990s.

A number of German scientists (such as Hermann Oberth) had fallen into the hands of the then Soviet Union and the path being followed was a similar one. The Golem I and II were put into service, considered purely

WITH ITS OWN PERSONALITY
The Vanguard class submarines have external characteristics, which give them their own personality; the superstructure, which supports the bow diving planes, along with its distinct conning tower position and size.

and simply to be perfected versions of the German V-2, later abandoned in favor of the Scud-A (1957), a SSM missile which achieved international renown in 1990 as a result of the war against Iraq.

The first Russian SLBM missiles were the SS-N-4 in 1958 and SS-N-5 (Sark) in 1963, later followed by the SS-N-6 (Serb) in 1967 and SS-N-8 (Sawfly) in 1973. Today Russia has the SS-N-20 (Sturgeon), SS-N-23 (Skiff) and SS-N-28 (Grom).

North American SSBMs

Almost immediately after putting the first nuclear submarine the U.S.S. Nautilus into service in 1954; the US Navy began a number of projects to introduce Skipjack class nuclear attack submarines, these entering service from 1960.

Simultaneously and in the record time of only two years, five of these boats were modified by cutting them in half and adding a cylinder almost 40 metres long. At the same time a lower casing was also fitted, allowing them to carry 16 vertical tubes for Polaris A1 missiles. These then became the George Washington class, and were operational from 1959. This was at the height of the cold war and just before the Russian-American Cuban missile crisis in 1962. The next class of submarine was the Ethan Allen, somewhat bigger, and operational from 1961 carrying Polaris A-2 missiles.

The next classes were La Fayette and Benjamin Franklin, a total of 13 ships. The first of which carried the Polaris A-2 missile and the others the A-3. These were bigger vessels, both in dimensions and in displacement, than the previous two classes; they entered service between 1963 and 1967.

The latest and most powerful of the SSBN

SUBTYPES OF THE SSBM DELTA CLASS

There are three distinct subtypes of the Russian SSBM Delta class: the IV armed with 16 SS-N-23 missiles as it's main weapon; the III with 16 SS-N-18 missiles and the I with 12 SS-N-8 missiles. They have similar external appearances, with the missile tubes located behind the conning tower and inside the raised superstructure. In the photograph we can see a Delta IV.

STRATEGIC MISSILES

The main weapons used by SSBM's are strategic missiles armed with multiple thermo-nuclear warheads. These missiles can reach up to 12,000 km with inertial satellite guidance systems, GPS or similar, with great precision. This accuracy is of the order of a few meters CEP (Circular Error Probability). In the photograph a French M-4 is shown.

class is the Ohio, with 18 vessels in total, the first of which entered service in 1981 and the last in 1997. All of these use the Trident 1 C4 missile or the Trident II D5 armed with 24 missiles instead of the 16 missiles normally carried by the rest of these vessels. They are estimated to have an active service life of some 25-30 years, which means that none of them are expected to be replaced until 2006-11.

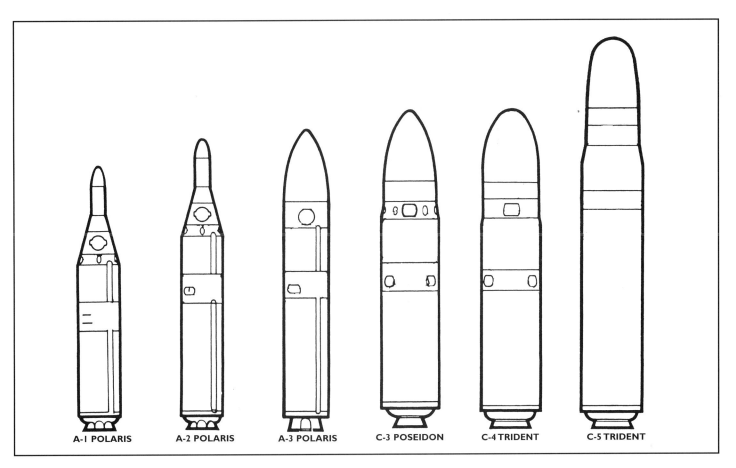

| A-I POLARIS | A-2 POLARIS | A-3 POLARIS | C-3 POSEIDON | C-4 TRIDENT | C-5 TRIDENT |

British SSBNs

The Royal Navy planned and built, from the mid 1960s, a much more modest fleet of SSBN's. This was when its four Resolution class submarines began entering service armed with 16 Polaris A3 missiles. These remained in service until fairly recently when they gradually began being replaced by the Vanguard class. This group consists of four ships, the last of which is to be delivered in 1999, with an armament of 16 Trident II D5 missiles.

French SSBNs

The French Republic has, since the times

SLBM MISSILES
The development of the Russian and American SLBM family of missiles.

LE TRIOMPHANT
The French Triomphant class have two directional rudders aft of the diving planes (at the stern of the vessel). In addition they do not use a conventional propeller, but instead use a pump-jet or multi-bladed propeller connected to a diffuser.

of General de Gaulle's "force de frappe", maintained a reduced fleet of ballistic missile nuclear submarines. This fleet came into being in 1971 when the first of five *Redoutable* class ships entered service. The construction of the others carried on through the 1970s and the beginning of the 1980s. These are now being replaced by the more modern "Le Triomphant" class which are now entering service. The last and fourth vessel, still without a name, is being programmed for delivery in the year 2007.

The French SSBN's are armed with 16 missiles produced and designed in France: the M4/TN 70 or 71 in the Redoutable's and the M45/TN 75 in the Triomphant's (manufactured by the company Aerospatiale).

Russian SSBNs

The road followed by the Russians to build up a strategic submarine fleet was different to that followed by Western Navies. At the outset they began with conventional submarines armed with a small number of missiles which where carried in the conning tower instead of the hull.

The first SSB was the Zulu V, a conventional submarine, with only two SS-N-4 missiles, which were launched when the vessel was on the surface. This was followed by Golf class vessels with SS-N-4, 5 or 8 missiles, including some that are able to use SS-N-20 missiles, which were going through evaluation trials. These vessels used three propellers.

The next class the Hotel, are nuclear powe-red. These continued with the missile tubes located in the conning tower, using the same missile model as the Golf in small quantities. The total number never exceeding 6. It had a twin propulsion unit with two reactors, two turbines, and two propellers. These vessels were in service between 1961 and 1980.

The Yankee class entered service from 1968 onwards, with more than thirty going into ser-vice. These boats were armed with the missiles contained the hull behind the conning tower, where a significant superstructure had been provided. The number of missiles increased to 18 SS-N-17 or SS-N-16. They had twin propulsion units. These boats continued to be built until 1974.

The penultimate class was the Delta, of which four different versions were known, totalling forty boats. In this class the missile tubes are positioned between the hull and the

A POWERFUL SUBMARINE

Large missile launching nuclear sub-marines of the Ohio class are the most powerful submarines ever constructed. Their deterrence strategy is based on 24 missiles, each of which is equipped with 12 thermo-nuclear warheads.

superstructure, aft of the conning tower with twelve missiles for the Delta I class and 16 for the Delta II, III & IV class. The missiles vary from the SS-N-8 to the SS-N-18 or SS-N-23. Nearly all of them are still in service. The first ship of this class was delivered in 1972 and the last in 1992. The whole of the outer casing is

A COMPARISON OF CHARACTERISTICS

CLASS/QTY	DELIVERY YEAR	DIMENSIONS	DISPL. SUB.	PROPULSION	ENGINES	POWER	SPEED/RANGE	WEAPONRY
Ohio (18)	1981/1997	171 x 13 x 11	18,750	Reactor GE PWR S8G	General Electric Electric (2)	60,000	25-nuclear	24 SLBM Trident I/II 4 x 533 mm LT tubes
Vanguard (4)	1993/1999	150 x 13 x 12	15,900	RR PWR 2 Reactor	GEC Turbines (2)	55,000	25-nuclear	16 SLBM Trident II 4 x 533 mm LT tubes
Le Triomphant	1997/2007	138 x 12 x 12	14,335	PWR K15 Reactor (turbo-electrical)	Motor eléc. (1)	41,5000	25-nuclear	16 SLBN M45/TN 75 4 x 533 LT tubes with Exocet missiles
Borey (1)	2003	170 x 13 x 10,5	17,000	PWR Reactor (2)	Turbines (2)	NC	26-nuclear	12 SLBN SS-N-28 o SS-N-23 6 x 533 LT tubes with ASW SS-N-15 & torpedos
Typhoon (6)	1981/1989	171 x 25 x 13	26,500	PWR VM-5 Reactors (2)	Turbines (2)	81,600	25-nuclear	20 SLBN SS-20. SAM SA-N-8. 4 x 650 mm LT tubes and 2 x 533 with SS-N-15 missiles and torpedos
Delta (20) (various types)	1985/1992	166 x 12 x 8.7	13,500	PWR VM-4 Reactors (2)	GT3A-365 Turbines (2)	37,400	24-nuclear	16/12 SLBN (different types) 4 x 533 LT tubes with ASW SS-N-15 missiles and torpedos

fitted with a layer of anechoic material to reduce noise and other emissions; it has twin propulsion units and in the classes II, III & IV there are two emergency engines.

Typhoon class vessels are the biggest submarines to have ever been constructed for any navy, with a submerged displacement greater than 25,000 tons. Its design is not a common one, in essence they are two Delta class submarines joined together by one hull, with 20 SS-N-20 missiles located forward of the conning tower, the only submarines to do so. The two nuclear power plants are contained within each hull; these power steam turbines which in turn are connected to two propellers. The rounded shape and retractable bow hydroplanes allow them to emerge without any problems from the Arctic ice fields and without fear of being trapped by them. The first ship entered service in December 1981 and the sixth and last in September 1989.

The latest Russian submarine known of is the Borey class, or type 955. Its size and presence are similar, up to a point, to that of the Ohio class, with one driving propeller and twin turbines. The missile tubes have returned to a position behind the conning tower (which itself is located forward on the vessel) and housed within the superstructure.

AN ENORMOUS SUBMARINE

Typhoons, or type 941s, are the largest submarines ever constructed and do not seem likely to ever be surpassed. Their reinforced steering components as well as the rounded shape of their hulls and retractable diving planes indicate that these vessels have been designed to operate in ice fields of up to 3 meters thickness.

It has only 12 missiles in comparison with 20 on the Typhoon, which uses the SS-N-23 or SS-N-28. Its construction began on the 2nd of November 1996 at the Severodvinsk shipyards and is expected to be in service by the year 2003.

The name of the first vessel is known- the Yuri Dolgoruky, and it is possible that two or three submarines will be constructed with three years between each of them. The rest of the technical information available is only speculation.

MAD

Magnetic Anomaly Detectors (MAD) installed in airplanes and helicopters mean that submerged submarines can be discovered. In this photograph we can see the U.S.S West Virginia being de-magnetised at the Kings Bay base.

Given the constant advances in technology, the conventional submarines of tomorrow, known as 4th generation models, are already being worked on. These are vessels, which will have features and levels of performance even more spectacular than those of the third generation, with prices to suit.

New submarines

All the major submarines designers who are preparing their projects at the moment are doing so with the realization that in the near future the market for these vessels will not only be considerable, but that it will also represent an enormous amount of money. So much so in fact, that in some cases it could represent a shipyard's viability or even a particular industry. With the components and work involved in these submarines amounting to a huge level of R & D. The construction of a submarine can last some years and in the case of building a complete series of vessels the time period can be more than a decade.

Although all specialist shipyards for the construction of vessels of this type never give up trying to win the bids there are some, which for one reason or another, are better suited than the rest for a particular project. As such it is better

LATERAL SWEEP SONARS
Another defining characteristic of these vessels is the extensive use of lateral sweep sonar systems such as those used in the Australian Collins class submarine (shown in the photograph), constructed from the Swedish Kockums project.

SNORKEL
The snorkel consists of two different parts, an inlet duct to allow atmospheric air to flow to both the inside of the submarine and diesel engine, and an outlet duct to allow the exhaust fumes to escape together with the foul air from the interior of the submarine. In the photograph we can see the extendible Snorkel used on the Dutch submarine, Walrus.

to talk about some particular types than others.

Different types

A variety of fourth generation submarines have been designed and offered to customers with some now entering the initial construction phase. However, there are relatively few at the moment, because some have still not had

their role and equipment outfits settled. In the case of Germany & Italy there is the 212 class.

for Spain & France the Scorpene and Agosta 90B; for the Netherlands the Moray; for Italy the 1300/1; for Russia the 636 & 1650 and for Sweden the A-19/Gotland.

Not all the submarines being constructed for the immediate future (although still considered to be fourth generation vessels) will have the base characteristics and special features distinguishing some of them from the others. For example, submarines with AIP (Air Independent Propulsion) systems and permanent magnet motors, which in some ways are being constructed as they go along. In addition, not every country wants to have identical boats to other countries. As such the Scorpene's ordered by Chile and being constructed by the joint venture Bazan/DCN will not have AIP, but instead it appears that they will have the same components as those being built in Spain for the Spanish Navy.

Particular curiosities

Although these vessels have a whole series of basic differences when compared to those of the third generation, the two most significant ones are with respect to the AIP system and the new permanent magnet electric motors.

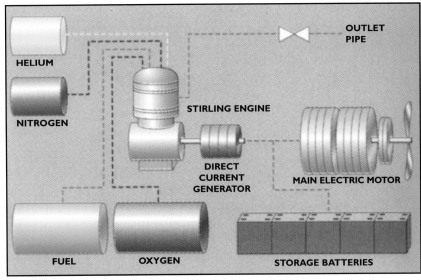

STIRLING ENGINE

The heat engine, turns out to very suitable in AIP systems because of the low vibration and sound levels. In the photograph is the AIP system used by the Swedish Gotlands.

TRIALS

A lot of the components to be used in fourth generation submarines go through trials in existing vessels. The German submarine U-17/S-196 is shown in this photograph and it is possible to see the extendible snorkel next to the periscope and radar.

With respect to the systems used for warfare and living, it is important to consider the standard use of towed sonar, commonly referred to as "stalker" and the extensive use of lateral sonar's. Additionally, also recognizing the increase in information systems and their automation in both combat and control. As a result of these changing trends the number of men and women on board is being considerably reduced. This is a point that should not be overlooked, because the result is that there is more space for the remaining personnel which can lead to improvements in the living conditions. Again it should not be forgotten

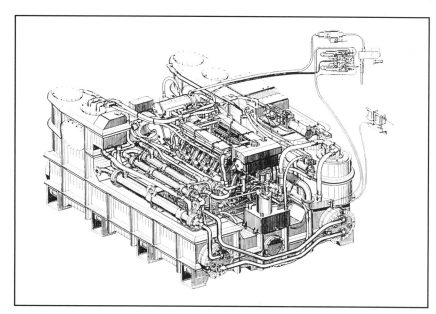

that in a submarine the idea of comfort is something which is very relative.

Air Independent Propulsion Systems (AIPs)

AIP systems have been used on submarines for a long time, these being based on banks of batteries. It is well established that this system increases the amount of time a submarine can spend under water without compromising its presence.

It should be noted that AIP systems are not trying to increase the vessel's maximum speed underwater or increase the absolute range. The aim of the AIP system is to considerably increase the range when running silently or increase the time it can be lying in wait, for which it is not necessary to provide great amounts of power, even in bursts for a short period of time. Instead what it does provide is a relatively small amount of power, but continually and in a way which means that it can proceed at a given power level for more days than it could do using the batteries only. In the future anti-submarine warfare involving another submarine will come down to a trade off which needs great patience. The loser will be the one who makes the first mistake or who for whatever reason has to show some sign of life.

Similar units, but different

There are five (four plus one) main AIP systems being considered: the MESMA/Module d'Energie Sous Marin Autonome, the energy cell, the Stirling engine and the closed circuit diesel engine. The first is being developed by the French DCN and the Spanish State Company Bazán. The second by

AIP SYSTEM

This is a theoretical schematic of an AIP closed circuit diesel system. This method is the least used at the moment and is still not completely developed.

AIP SYSTEMS ON THE GOTLANDS

Although the Swedish Gotlands will probably see considerable modifications before being considered as fourth generation submarines, they are one of the few classes, which are powered on a day to day with AIP systems on board.

the Germans, the third by the Swedes who have carried out trials with it on some of their existing submarines and the fourth whose origins have to be looked for in German projects from the second world war- types XXIX, XXXIII, XXXIV, 227 and Delphin. The fifth involves the traditional battery, but using new types with greater power.

The MESMA consists of a turbine, which operates with gas obtained from a primary circuit or combustion chamber using a mixture of ethanol and oxygen. The power generated by the turbine can be used to drive a generator to power an electric motor, or instead to directly drive the propeller. This system is very quiet and triples the range underwater.

The energy cell can basically be described as an inverse electrolytic reaction. From oxygen and hydrogen electricity, heat and water are obtained. The electricity is directly used by the engine or battery, the heat is applied to any appropriate purpose and the water, which is chemically pure, is used for drinking and washing purposes or expelled from the submarine.

The Stirling engine is an old and well known system, but which until fairly recently had not been given much attention. It is similar to the combustion engine, but produces much less vibration, noise and pollution. As such being used in submarine applications where reductions in vibration and noise are so important, it is an extremely welcome development.

The closed circuit diesel engine consists of the standard engine with a filter unit incorporated in the outlet, as well as oxygen being delivered to the combustion chamber. With this system there are no exhaust gases and the engine becomes an independent unit, although not managing to completely avoid the vibration and noise produced by the combustion explosions.

There are a variety of new types of batteries, although those, which seem to have the best possibilities, are called LAIS (Lithium Aluminium/Iron Sulphide). These produce something in the order of 300% more energy per unit weight (100Wh/kg against 35 Wh/kg) than the best and most modern Ac/Pb (actinium/lead) batteries, but also generate a greater amount of heat.

The Permanent Magnet Motor

This type of motor has a greater capacity for working with fewer coils than normal. In addition, it does not have brushes and has the permanent magnets located on the rotor with the coils on the stator, the magnetic field being changed through converters. It is much more compact, incorporates better cooling properties and can be used in a closed circuit, directly with water.

The increase in the torque allows the use of

SONIC SENSORS
Sound travels better and over much longer distances in water than in the air, for which reason sonic sensors are used as a way of detecting and combating a submarine under water. Because of this these vessels are equipped with sensitive, large sensors, as used by this German submarine whose wake shows the presence of a sonar dome.

SONIC TRACKERS
Sonic trackers are beginning to be used more and more widely, with the advantage that they prevent the submarine from capturing its own noise signals. They are towed at distances of several hundred meters behind the submarine to ensure that its own echoes do not mask those of other vessels.

propellers with a greater diameter/pitch, which means that the noise level is reduced as well as the possibilities of cavitation. This torque level originates from the greater permanent magnetic fields produced as a result of using new development work based on the use of Samarium and Neodymium, two very rare elements.

The weight and volume are substantially less than that of a conventional motors, these being 60% and 40% less respectively.

At the moment a Jeumont model (French) is available, called the EPSM2 and it is believed that there will soon be another from Siemens (German), called the Permasyn.

MOTOR

The motors used by 4th generation vessels will, in general, be the new electronic/synchronous permanent magnet type, such as this 1,800 kW ESM2 from the French company Jeumont, going through some trials.

THE CONNING TOWER

The conning tower contains the mast, antennas, periscopes and snorkel. The emission of exhaust gases can be done directly when the vessel is at periscope depth via part of the snorkel tube- as shown in this photograph, on the after side of the conning tower.

CONTROL ROOM

In modern submarines each and every one of the vessels sensors and weapons are controlled from this room. This also includes the propulsion engines (diesel and/or motors), batteries, snorkel and maneuvering operations.

AIP MODULE

Fourth generation submarines will be delivered with or without AIP modules, this depending on the needs of the purchaser. The AIP module could be incorporated on board the vessel during the original construction phase or later, depending on the case, although always in the ideal position. The propulsion heat engines will be controlled by electronic and information command systems. The management systems will be centralized, with instructions coming from the control room.

HABITABILITY

The living conditions of fourth generation submarines, although austere and with little space, will offer conditions as comfortable as they possibly could be in these types of vessels.

SCORPENE CLASS SUBMARINE

This is a view of what the Scorpène class submarines will probably look like, designed and constructed by the Spanish State company Bazán and the French company DCN (Direction des Constructions Navales).

TORPEDO ROOM

The torpedo rooms of fourth generation submarines are specially designed for the easy handling and loading of the tubes, using lifts, winches and mobile gantries, controlled from the chief operator's desk.

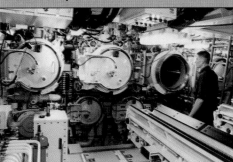

TORPEDO CHARGE

Torpedos for reloading arrive at the right place through the corresponding hatch, easily positioned and comfortably stowed in their mountings, at the time when they are due to be loaded into the tubes, virtually without any human intervention.

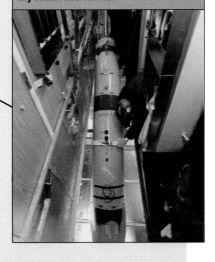

BATTERIES

The batteries used on board these vessels will not be the same as the type traditionally used, with lead plates and sulphuric acid (as used on automobiles). Instead these submarines will use new technology (LAIS etc), but with a similar number of elements (some 400).

A COMPARISON OF CHARACTERISTICS

CLASS/QTY	YEAR DELIVERED	DIMENSIONS	DISPL. SUB.	PROPULSION	ENGINES	POWER	SPEED/RANGE	WEAPONRY
212 (4+2)	2003/2006	56 x 7 x 6	1,830	Diesel/elect. +AIP	P.M. Motor electronic	4,243	20-420/8	6 x 533 mm LT tubes
636 (NC)	not known (NK)	74 x 9,9 x 6.2	2,350	Diesel/elect. +AIP	Electric Motor	2,830 aprox.	17-280/4	6 x 533 mm LT tubes
1300/1 (NC)	NK	60 x NK x NK	1,500 approx	Diesel/electric +AIP	Electric Motor	NK	20-400/3	6 x 533 mm LT tubes
Scorpène (7)	2002/2008	62 x 6 x NK	1,565	Diesel/elect. +AIP	Electric Motor	NK	>20-536/4	6 x 533 mm LT tubes
Moray (NC)	NK	60 x 6.4 x 5.5	1,545	Diesel/elect. +AIP	Electric Motor	3 x 2,200	20-200/2	6 x 533 mm LT tubes
Gotland (3)	NK	60 x 6 x 5.6	1,490	Diesel/elect. +AIP	Electric Motor	NK	20-NK	4 x 533 mm LT tubes +2 x 400 mm

The submarine's traditional weapon was the torpedo, a device first developed in 1886 by the British inventor Robert Whitehead, in Trieste, then a part of Austria. After a series of improvements it achieved complete reliability, sinking thousands of ships over the last hundred years or so.

The air torpedo

From the very beginning the propulsion system for the torpedo was based on compressed air stored under pressure in a tank. Reheating this air increases the pressure and power produced in the propulsion system, with the torpedo following a path in its characteristic way, leaving a wake, which is easily identifiable. To prevent it from rotating

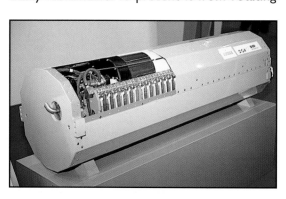

EXOCET SM-39

This view shows an Exocet SM-39 torpedo from the rear.

BATTERY

This photograph shows the propulsion unit for a French F-17 torpedo. The battery is AgO/Zn (Silver Oxide/Zinc) type with a KOH (Potassium hydroxide) electrolyte.

about its own axis it was designed with two counter-rotation propellers on a double shafted arrangement.

For navigation purposes it was designed with a gyroscope as well as hydrostatic plate, which acted to maintain it at the correct depth on route to its target. Both of these controlled the relevant fins at the tail of the torpedo changing the position depending on the situation.

The warhead, at the front of the torpedo, contained the explosive charge and fuse (or component which ignites the explosives) with two kinds of effect, these normally being an explosion on contact or in close proximity to the target.

The electric torpedo

Towards the end of the Second World War different countries were developing the electric torpedo, although with many problems. With this weapon the compressed air propulsion system was replaced by a series of batteries, with the result that the telltale wake was greatly diminished. Although the propulsion system was replaced by an electric one, the navigation and guidance systems remained very much as they were.

They are easily distinguished by their external appearance with the nozzle at the stern betraying what type it is. This type of system is very efficient and silent, which is the reason it is also used to propel submarines.

It consists of a multi-bladed propeller (12 or more blades) which rotates inside a nozzle. A diffuser is housed at the extreme end of the nozzle to straighten out the helical stream of water coming from the propeller. In this case there is only one, not two counter-rotating propellers, this system forces the water to flow in a straight line.

The diffuser is made up of fixed fins in curved and profiled shapes, the number of which always exceeds the number of blades on the propeller.

This type of torpedo had a smaller range and speed than those with the air system, but its discretion with regards to its wake, making the submarine's position more difficult to discover, make it a more preferable type for many commanders.

TORPEDO F-17

The loading of an F-17 model 1 guided torpedo onto a submarine through the torpedo hatch.

Other propulsion systems

Both historically and in the present day other propulsion systems have been and are being used in torpedos. For example there is the turbine, or closed circuit heat engine, or in a certain number of electrical propulsion units the difference is in the type of battery supplying the power.

Germany experimented with a variety of different types of propulsion technology during the Second World War. These were systems using hydrogen peroxide, the closed circuit engine, and the so-called gas engine and rocket propulsion.

At the moment the most usual type of propulsion unit is electric, using batteries. This is the case with the Mu-90/Impact which has an electro-chemical cell made of silver oxide (the cathode), an aluminium alloy (the anode) and powdered sodium hydroxide which reacts instantly when the cell fills up with salt water. This is a very safe system, which cannot start operating until it has been launched from its tube.

Pumpjet propulsion system

This modern propulsion system, the pumpjet, is used in both torpedos and submarines.

PROPULSION

Here is a view of the pumpjet propulsion system used in many modern day torpedos.

Programmed torpedos

During the last phase of the Second World War German technology led to the introduction of a new torpedo for its submarines. The originality of this torpedo was not in its propulsion system, but in its ability to be programmed to follow a set route. After being pre-programmed and then launched it would begin a series of turns and loops, then go back to its original destination before finally hitting the enemy ship. This type of system continues to be used today along with other innovations, such as acoustic torpedos.

The acoustic torpedo

This auto-control system is one of the most commonly used at the moment, especially in anti-submarine torpedos. This torpedo is equipped with a special head incorporating a passive sonar unit, which allows it to capture the sounds of its target and then orientate itself accordingly. It is also often equipped with an

active sonar which captures a ships echo, something which the opponent would find easy enough to counteract by using an acoustic decoy.

The majority of submarines are of this type.

The wire-guided torpedo

One of the systems most used these days, especially in anti-ship torpedos is the wire-guided and controlled torpedo. It is guided through a combination of manual and instrumentation control, using a long cable, which extends up to 30 km or more. This cable allows the transmission of commands.

It is not unusual for such a torpedo to also include an active or active/passive acoustic search head.

Gyroscopic control

As far as the first effective guidance system is concerned this still continues being used in many torpedos for particular types of mission. For example, as used in the Russian Shkval, a very special, high speed torpedo with a nuclear warhead. It is the fastest known of at the moment with a rocket engine, which gives it a maximum speed of 200 knots (370 km/hour), although with a range of only 10 miles.

POSEIDON C-3

The Poseidon C-3 ballistic missile is carried by American nuclear submarines.

THE TORPEDO ROOM

This torpedo room in the bow of a Russian Whiskey class submarine was in service during the 1950s and a part of the 1960s. The four hatches can be clearly seen as well as the stowing gantries on the deck and on the bulkheads.

Torpedo sizes used

Although at the outset the diameter of the first torpedo was 356 mm, military necessities have demanded that this be increased to 533 mm, a size that has now become the standard.

However, during the Second World War the Japanese used a larger sized torpedo with devastating results. At present different sizes exist together, and in practice have established themselves as the most usual types. As such there is the 324mm used for anti-submarine missions, the 533 & 550mm for anti-ship work and the 650mm Russian torpedo (type 65), specially designed for anti-ship missions.

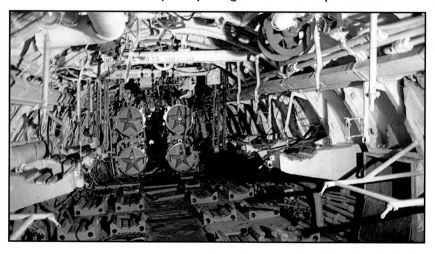

Mines

Historically, the mine has been one of the submarine's most insidious weapons and continues to be widely used in the present day. Mines can be laid from surface ships or aircraft, but one of the most commonly used methods is by submarine.

There are many different types and sizes in existence with a variety of characteristics, although most of these have to correspond to the diameter of the launching tubes, these being the means by which they are laid.

Missiles

There are three main types of missiles, which can be launched from submarines: Submarine Launched Ballistic Missiles (SLBM's), anti-ship missiles (SSM's) such as the Harpoon and Exocet, and Submarine Launched Cruise Missiles (SLCM's) such as the Tomahawk. These are the most well known Western models, but in addition there are the Russian SS-N-21 Sampson and SS-N-15 Starfish, launched from 533 mm tubes and the SS-N-16 Stallion launched from 650 mm tubes.

Some Russian submarines can also use SAM missiles like the SA-N-5 Grail and the SA-N-8 Strela.

Encapsulated missiles

To launch a missile from a submerged submarine, whether it be ballistic, cruise or anti-

EXTERNAL TUBE HATCHES
With this Kilo class Indian submarine, the Sindhughosh, we can see the two external hatches at the front of the submarine for the upper torpedo launch tubes.

DETAILS
In this air driven American example there are some notable features, such as the central outlet for air bubbles at the tail end, the fin/cross arrangement and twin propeller.

ship, is an operation which is carried out in a way which is completely different to that on dry land. A ground launch is something that is quite well known to most people, with so many space launches having taken place. However on board a submarine a missile has to be propelled from its tube by using compressed air in such a way that at the correct moment the capsule protecting it is opened. This is then followed by the missile's engines firing, and it setting out on its flight.

The missile's fins and control components remain in a retracted position inside the capsule and are only opened up when the missile's engine is ignited.

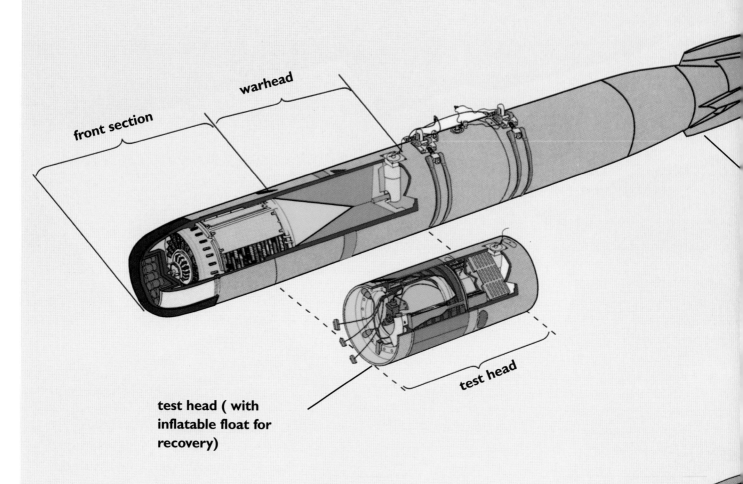

front section

warhead

test head (with
inflatable float for
recovery)

test head

Tail unit (for torpedos
launched from the
surface)

Tail

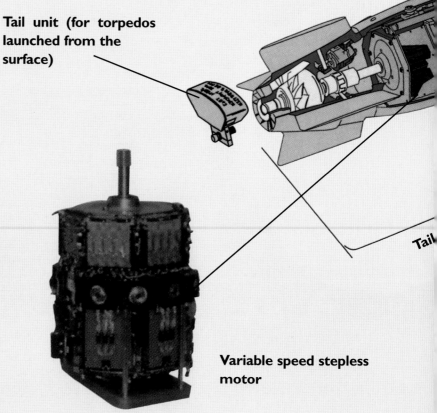

Variable speed stepless
motor

MAIN CHARACTERISTICS

OPERATIONAL REQUIREMENTS

Suitable against submarines in shallow waters.

Nuclear, operating in deep waters.

Carrying out evasive actions.

Both types equipped with anechoic protection.

OPERATIONAL CHARACTERISTICS

Launched at depths not greater than 30 m.

Speeds not less than 29 knots and not greater than 50 knots.

Range greater than 10 km at maximum speed.

Range of 25 km at minimum speed.

Able to operate in depths of up to 1,000 m.

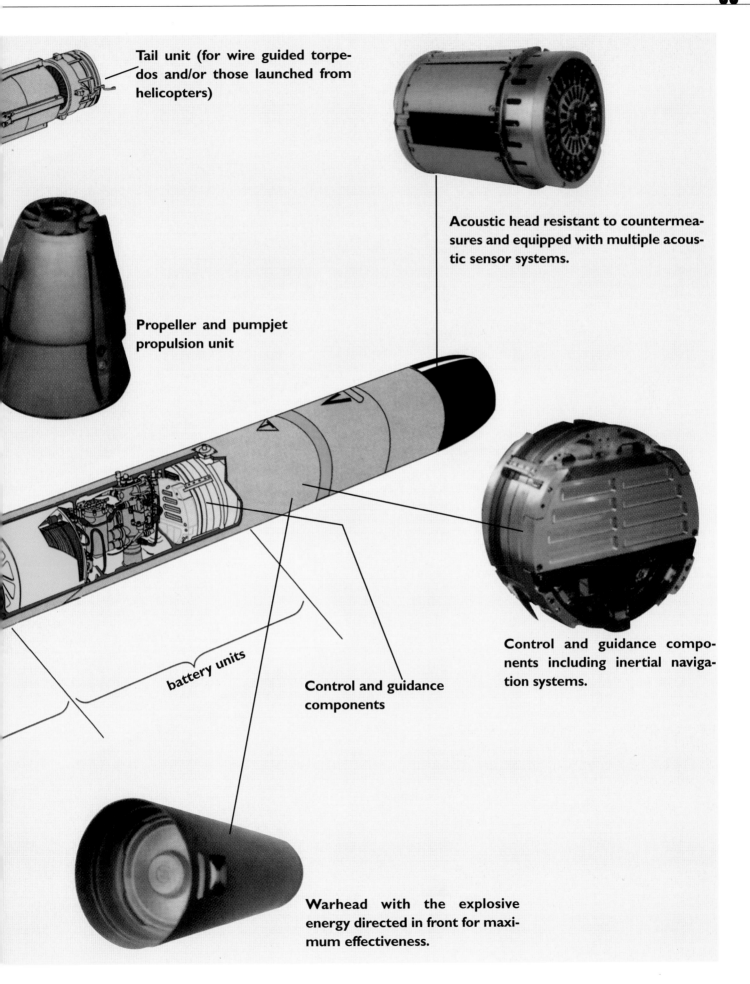

Tail unit (for wire guided torpe-dos and/or those launched from helicopters)

Acoustic head resistant to countermea-sures and equipped with multiple acous-tic sensor systems.

Propeller and pumpjet propulsion unit

battery units

Control and guidance components

Control and guidance compo-nents including inertial naviga-tion systems.

Warhead with the explosive energy directed in front for maxi-mum effectiveness.

E ver since the sinking of the C-3 submarine in the middle of the Spanish civil war by the German U-26, this type of vessel has been adapted to become one of the best ways of fighting against the submarine.

The SSK concept

For decades the submarine was considered to be the ideal vessel for both attacking merchant ships and being involved in surface attacks. But during the Second World War the American submarine U.S.S. Batfish, in only four days, detected, chased and sank three Japanese submarines. This brought to light that in a global anti-submarine war the importance of the submarine could be considerable. The arrival of the nuclear submarine with its high speed & unique features (combined with other very special characteristics) was an extremely important moment with, in practice, every nuclear submarine offering anti-submarine characteristics.

The attack submarine

At the beginning of 1955 the U.S.S. Nautilus entered service, the first nuclear submarine in history, and as such the first true submarine, incorporating the beginning of new hull designs which would be adopted for future vessels. The

---

HULL

French nuclear attack submarines present some small external differences to other vessels, in particular when referring to the shape of the hull. The photograph shows the Emeraude, which has a more hydrodynamic hull than the Rubis, the first in the series.

DIFFERENCES

Submarines in the second of the Los Angeles subclass, SSN 751 to 773 have their hydroplanes at the bow and not on the conning tower, as well as 12 VLS's on the forward side of the tower in the sequence 2-4-4-2. In the photograph, the U.S.S. Alexandria SSN-757 is preparing to moor at the quayside after completing a voyage.

---

union of the nuclear propulsion system and this new hull design led to the creation of the U.S.S. Skipjack, a nuclear attack submarine which entered service in 1959. This vessel had a speed of more than 30 knots, a record, which remained unbeaten until the delivery of the new Los Angeles class in 1976.

At the moment a submerged submarine can launch encapsulated SSM missiles from its torpedo tubes in addition to the new Tomahawk cruise missiles, or in the case of the corresponding Russian SS-Ns from their vertical missile

tubes. The mission objectives have diversified considerably for all submarines. This is something that has been reduced considerably in recent, with the distinction being more along the lines of two categories: nuclear attack submarines (SSN's) and ballistic missile nuclear submarines (SSBN's). There are clear and distinct differences between both of these types.

Present day SSN's

At the present moment there are three Western countries with nuclear attack submarines: the USA, France and Great Britain. As far as

THE FRENCH RUBIS

The French Rubis, such as the *Amethyste* S-605, also presented some differences between the first and last vessels. The first four were subject to modifications as a result of operation Amethyste (AMElioration Tactique Hydrodynamique Silence Transmission Ecoute) in which specific aspects were improved and the external appearance was altered.

those countries which faced the West in the past are concerned only the Russian and Chinese fleets have such vessels, with Russia having many more than China.

The SSN's of the US Navy

The American attack submarine fleet was created in 1959 with six Skipjack class vessels, one of which was lost in an accident in May 1968. They used a Westinghouse S5W pressurised water reactor and had six 533 mm torpedo tubes. They did not launch missiles.

The next class was the Thresher with 14 submarines, the lead ship of the series being lost on the 10th of April 1963 along with her entire crew of 112 plus 17 civilian contractors, when she was carrying out trials at maximum depth. These vessels used the Westinghouse S5W reactor. They were armed with four torpedo tubes which could also fire SSM encapsulated Harpoon missiles and entered service from 1962 onwards.

The Sturgeon class, in practice a remodelled Thresher, consisted of 37 vessels. These boats had modifications made to those areas of the submarine that effected its sailing under ice (e.g. the conning tower hydroplanes could rotate 90 degrees until they were vertical). There were also a variety of other specific changes.

ANECHOIC TILES

The British Trafalgar class has been given a second skin of anechoic tiles, which result in a reduced possibility of being detected by active sonar. In this photograph of the Trafalgar in summer 1998 a large number of the tiles have fallen off.

The reactor used was a Westinghouse S5W. Her four torpedo tubes could launch the Harpoon and the new Tomahawk missiles. The first vessel of the series was delivered in 1967 and the last in 1975. Some of these later submarines were equipped with BQS-13 towed sonar.

The next class was the Los Angeles with 53 vessels, the delivery beginning in 1976 and continuing up to 1996, all of which are still in active service. They were constructed to combat the Soviet Victor class (1967) and used the new S6G General Electric reactor. From the 12th ship of this class, the U.S.S Providence, in addition

OPERATIONAL TRAFALGARS

Of the seven Trafalgar class submarines, there are normally only five operational at any time. The other two are normally undergoing a refit together in a large dry dock.

SEAWOLF

The Seawolfe class has surpassed the Los Angeles class both in performance and price.

to being able to fire encapsulated Harpoon and Tomahawk missiles from the 533mm torpedo tubes, they were fitted with 12 vertical tubes for Tomahawk missiles. They are located outside the pressure hull, between the conning tower and the BQQ sonar.

The latest SSN class in the US Navy is the Seawolf (3 vessels plus 3 others which are similar), of which only the first is at sea. The sixth vessel is expected to be delivered in 2005. A Westinghouse S6W is used in the first three and a General Electric S9G will be fitted in the other three vessels. The weaponry on board can be re-configured and they have the capacity to carry up to 50 commandos. These submarines can reach a silent speed of 20 knots and their weaponry consists of Gould Mk 48 wire guided torpedos, Harpoon & Tomahawk missiles and up to 100 mines in lieu of torpedos. The military effectiveness of this class of vessel is considered to be three times that of the Los Angeles. They have eight tubes with a larger diameter than normal, 673mm, positioned in the centre of the vessel. They were designed to face the threat represented by Russian submarines, but the high price of one thousand million dollars each, together with the reduction in the threat posed by a Russian enemy has led to the reduction in the initial number of submarines required. The initial number of vessels in the series was thirty.

The French SSNs

France designed its nuclear submarine fleet in a distinct way, with the result that from the first moment all its efforts were dedicated to SSBN's instead of SSN's. It did not have any SSN's in service until the arrival of the Rubis/Amethyste, these being smaller in size than is usual for such vessels, and only 10 % bigger than the conventional Agosta class. The Rubis/Amethyste class are single propeller vessels supplied with an electric propulsion system in times of emergency.

Their weaponry consists of four torpedo tubes with encapsulated SSM Exocet SM 39 missiles, ECAN L5 mod. 3 torpedoes, which can be substituted by 32 FG 29 mines.

The British SSN's

H.M.S. Dreadnought, the Royal Navy's first nuclear submarine, was delivered in 1963 and followed in 1966 & 1971 by the five Valiant class and from 1973 up to 1981 by the six Swiftsure class. All of these are armed with 533mm tubes equipped with torpedos and Harpoon missiles as well as mines, which can be used in their place. The seven Trafalgar class succeeded these, armed with Harpoon and Tomahawk missiles as well as torpedos and mines (at the same time). At the moment all of the Trafalgar class boats are being kept operational as well as six of the Swiftsure class.

REFUELLING
The British "Ts" need to replenish their nuclear fuel every 12-15 years and are provided with retractable hydroplanes at the bow. In the photograph the H.M.S. Trenchant can be seen with a curious array of red lead marks, after returning from a long patrol.

A COMPARISON OF CHARACTERISTICS

CLASS/QTY	YEAR DELIVERED	DIMENSIONS	DISPL. SUB.	PROPULSION	ENGINES	POWER	SPEED/RANGE	WEAPONRY
Seawolf (6)	1997/2004	108 x 13 x 10.9	9,142	Reactor GE	Turbines (2)	45,000	38-nuclear	8 LT 660 mm tubes with SSM y SuW Tomahawk & Harpoon missiles; Mk-48 torpedos & mines
Los Angeles	1976/1996	110 x 10 x 10	6,927	Reactor GE	Turbines (2)	35,000	32-nuclear	VLS with Tomahawk missiles + 4 LT 553 mm tubes with SSM & SuW Tomahawk & Harpoon missiles; Mk 48 torpedos, Captor y Mobile
Trafalgar (7)	1982/1991	85 x 10 x 9.5	5,208	Reactor RR PWR 1	Turbines (2)	15,000	32-nuclear	5 LT 553 mm tubes with Tomahawk $ Sub-Harpoon missiles; Spearfish & Tigerfish torpedos & minas
Astute (3)	2002/2006	92 x 11 x 10	6,800	Reactor RR PWR 2	Turbogenerators (2)	NK	29-nuclear	5 LT 533 mm tubes with Tomahawk & Sub-Harpoon; missiles; Spearfish & Tigerfish torpedos & minas
Rubis	1983/1993 CAS 4B	74 x 8 x 6.4 (2)	2,670	Reactor PWR	Turbogenerators	9,500	25-nuclear	4 LT 533 mm tubes with Exocet missiles and ECAN L5 torpedos. Up to 14 FG 29 mines
Yasen (7)	2001/2004 (2)	111 x 12 x 8.4	8,600	Reactor PWR	Turbines GT3A	43,000	28-nuclear	VLS with SS-N-27 missiles 4 LT 650 & 2 LT 533 mm with SS-N-15 with missiles & torpedos
Akula (13)	1986/2000 VN-5	110 x 14 x 10.4 (2)	9,500	Reactor PWR	Turbines GT3A	47,600	28-nuclear	4 LT 650 mm & 4 533 mm tubes with SS-N-21, SS-N-15, & SS-N-16 missiles Torpedos, 6 additional TL 533 mm at bow area

REPAIRS

Because of the long duration of the tours, which can reach up to 90 days or even more, all attack submarines usually need repairs when they return to base as a result of the aggressiveness of the marine environment. In the photograph the conning tower of the Sturgeon class submarine U.S.S. Batfish is shown on its arrival back at base.

These will be replaced by the five Astute class, with work beginning on the first one in 1999 with it expected to be entering service in 2006. They will be an improved version of the Trafalgar, which will not need to be refuelled during its entire service life. They will use Harpoon, Tomahawk missiles and Spearfish torpedos.

The Russian SSN's

These vessels can be thought of as being amongst the most innovative of their type. The first boats had Titanium hulls, and were able to reach great depths with the capability to reach speeds of more than 40 knots underwater, thanks to their metal fusion reactors.

The saga associated with these vessels began with the November class, entering service between 1958 and 1963, with twin propellers, a high acoustic signature and armed only with torpedos and mines. The next Echo class was known of from 1962, vessels with significantly reduced acoustic signatures and which used two propellers with five blades.

The Victor class was a single shafted design, with two emergency propulsion systems and a hydrodynamic hull. There were three distinct series of this vessel, I, II & III, which entered service between 1967 and 1984, of which some of the class III vessels are still operational. Its weaponry consists of 533 & 650mm torpedos with some being armed with nuclear warheads, in addition

THE LOS ANGELES CLASS

Los Angeles class nuclear attack submarines were designed to counteract the Soviet Victor class vessels. This series is made up of two sub-classes, one with the hydroplane in the conning tower and without VLS forward of the conning tower. The second has the VLS and hydroplanes forward of the conning tower. In the photograph the U.S.S. Phoenix SSN 702 is shown.

to SS-N-21 & ASW SS-N-15 missiles (or with mines used instead of missiles or torpedos). Its maximum operational depth is 400 meters with a probable collapse depth of 600 meters.

Alfa class submarines entered service in 1970 and continued being delivered up to 1983. Its titanium alloy allowed it to reach depths of 700 meters; a depth never managed before. In addition it also greatly reduced its magnetic signature. Its two reactors use a bismuth-lead liquid metal coolant, which gives them a submerged speed in excess of 45 knots. Its weaponry consists of torpedos and SS-N-15 anti-submarine missiles. The combination of their speed and depth capability caused a great deal of concern in Western Navies. They were kept in operation until 1992/93.

The *Sierra* class was a link between the Alfa and Akula class, entering service between 1990 and 1993 and still remain in service. They are equipped with four 533mm tubes and others of 650mm, from which torpedos and missiles are launched, including those with nuclear warheads.

The Akulas are the latest SSN vessels to enter the Russian fleet, but with two of the 13 submarines making up the series still to be delivered. Its speed under water is only 28 knots, less than the Sierras, but at the same time they have improved acoustic and magnetic signatures. Its weaponry is similar.

The conventional submarine, far from being quashed by its nuclear cousin, has been greatly improved with increases in speed and range as well as quietness over the years.

Generation "O"

During the Second World War the submarine was technically speaking a submersible vessel more than a true submarine. German technological advances led to the development of new types of vessels- the XXI & XXIII for example, and the development of the so-called snorkel. This is a tube fitted with a series of valves which enables the submarine to sail underwater using the diesel engines to provide power and simultaneously charge the batteries. At the same time different anaerobic propulsion systems were being experimented with such as the Walter turbine, as well as different types of torpedos with programmed trajectories, acoustic or wire guided.

The 1st, 2nd & 3rd generations

Each and every one of the allied countries embarked on the design of their own vessels based on the Mk XXI/XXIII German submarines.

U-13/S-192

The photograph shows the U-13/S-192 German submarine (type 206-A), before being transferred to Indonesia where it was renamed the *Nagarangsang*. It is armed with eight 533mm LT tubes (8 torpedos or 16 mines) and can deploy up to another 24 mines from two GRP detachable lateral housings.

SNORKEL

The conning tower of the submarine *Zeeleeuw*, the second of the Walrus class, the forward edge is shown here with the distinctive snorkel diffuser clearly visible. These improve the vessel's ability to remain undetected during the battery charging phase, when underway at snorkel depth.

A good number of existing vessels were modified, increasing the battery capacity, providing them with snorkels, making the hull and conning tower more hydrodynamic and changing the propellers. Everything possible was done to increase the speed and range at the same time as reducing the acoustic signature.

The first submarines of this type are known as the 1st generation given that they are the most direct descendants of those German vessels described earlier. The most modern

conventional submarines, using diesel engines on the surface and electric ones when submersed, constitute the 3rd. This leaves the 2nd generation vessels, which are somewhere between the other two. It is not easy to define which fall into one category or the other with the vessels often mixing different features, according to the type, country and date of construction.

Exporting and nationalization

There are many countries which have submarines, but which do not have the technology not only to construct them, but in some cases to keep them operational.

As a result there are submarines which have been specially designed for export and which do not belong to one generation or another and are therefore not easy to categorise. For a variety of reasons these can incorporate some features from one category and different ones from another. This includes cases where vessels, even new ones, have been taken out of operational service in a particular navy because they have been sold to another country.

> **DIFFERENCES IN THE CONNING TOWERS**
>
> In this Pelosi, which appears here off duty and next to a Greek 209 vessel, the Glavkos S-110, the differences between the conning towers (the only part of the Glavkos visible) are quite striking. In this photograph we can see that one of the periscopes has been raised.

> **NAGGALA**
>
> German 209 class submarines have been constructed with particular attention to the export market and sales overseas, having obtained excellent operational results. In this picture we can see the Indonesian Naggala, sister ship of the Cakra, which entered service in 1981. It has the capability of sailing for 50 days without refuelling and is armed with eight 533mm LT tubes and AEG SUT Mod. O torpedos.

With regards to the export of submarines, or those which have ended up in other hands for one reason or another, the vessels being referred to are mainly those still in service at this moment. The different classes are: the German 206, 207, 209, 210 & 800; the Russian Foxtrot, Kilo & Romeo; the French Agosta & Daphne; the British Oberon, Upholder & 540; the Swedish Sjoormen; the North American Guppy II, III Tang and finally the Dutch Zwaardvis series.

The countries which are using them are: 206- Indonesia; 207- Denmark & Norway; 209; Argentina, Brazil, Chile, Columbia, Ecuador, Greece, India, Indonesia, Peru, Turkey & Venezuela; 210- Norway; 800- Israel; Foxtrot- Cuba, India, Libya, Poland, Ukraine; Kilo- Algeria, China, India, Poland & Rumania; Romeo- Bulgaria, North Korea, Egypt & China; Agosta- Pakistan; Daphne- Pakistan, Portugal & South Africa; Oberon- Australia, Brazil, Canada & Chile; Upholder- Canada; 540- Israel; Sjoormen- Singapore; Guppy II & III- Taiwan & Turkey; Tang- Turkey; Zwaardvis- Taiwan.

Those which continue in the hands of the country responsible for building them are the German 205 & 206; the Australian Collins; the North Korean Sang-Os; the Chinese Han, Song & Ming; the Spanish Delfin & Galerna; the French Agosta & Daphne; the Italian Pelosi & Sauro; the Japanese Ayashio, Harushio & Yuushio; the Dutch Walrus; the Russian Kilo, Tango & Foxtrot; the Swedish Gotland, Vastergotland & Nacken; the Turkish Preveze; the Yugoslav Sava & Heroj.

Taking all of these into consideration the total is something like 386 submarines, in other words

A COMPARISON OF CHARACTERISTICS

CLASS/QTY	YEAR DELIVERED	DIMENSIONS	DISPL. SUB.	PROPULSION	ENGINES	POWER	SPEED/RANGE	WEAPONRY
Galerna (4)	1983/1986	68 x 7 x 5.4	1,740	Diesel-electric	SEMT-Pielstick (2)	3,600	20-350/3.5	4 LT 533 mm tubes with torpedos and/or mines
S. Pelosi (4)	1988/1995	66 x 7 x 5.6	1,862	Diesel-electric	Finncantieri GMT 210.16 SM (3)	3,672	19-250/4	6 LT 533 mm tubes with torp. and possibility for missiles
Oyashio (5)	1998/2002	82 x 9 x 7.9	3,000	Diesel-electric	Kawasaki 12B 25S (2)	5,520	20-NK	6 LT 533 mm tubes with torpedos and Sub-Harpoon missiles
Walrus (4)	1992/1994	68 x 8 x 7	2,800	Diesel-electric	SEMT-Pielstick 12 PA4 200 VG (3)	6,300	20-NK	4 LT 533 mm tubes with torp. and Sub-Harpoon missiles
Kilo (4)	1982 aprox.	74 x 10 x 6.6	3,076	Diesel-electric	4-2AA-42M (2)	3,650	17-400/3	6 LT 533 mm ubes with torpedos and SAM SA-N-5/8
Gotland (3)	1996/1997	60 x 6 x 5.6	1,490	Diesel-electric+AIP	MTU diesel (2) Kockums V4-275R (2)	NK	20-NK	4 LT 533 mm tubes + 2 of 400, with torp. and/or mines

SALVATORI PELOSI

The Salvatori Pelosi appears here moored to a Baltic quay while it is off duty, in a break between exercises. The roundness of its hull and the width of its conning tower with respect to the deck is clearly visible in this photograph. We can see that the two periscopes are not in line, but are instead side by side.

THE ITALIAN NAZARIO SAURIOS

The Italian Nazario Sauro class vessels (the Feccia di Cossato is shown in this picture) are the predecessors of the Salvatori Pelosi, which are considered to be improved versions of the Sauros. In the photograph below the submarine is shown sporting its identification numbers, although normally identification as such is not used in those units employed by the navy.

The hull

A third generation submarine has a hydrodynamic hull with a single propeller, 5 or 7 bladed, with the aim being that the tail-cross only shows one blade at any time. The hull is completed by a conning tower on the upper part, where someone is always on look out duty when the vessel is sailing on the surface. Of course this is also where the different components such as the periscopes, snorkels and antennas are housed.

In some vessels there are double access hatches with a sluice gate, which allows them to operate with commando groups. In others the sluice gate can be located in one of the access hatches from the deck, though they can be omitted completely.

It is a matter of necessity to have a special hatch for loading torpedos. This hatch also doubles as a sluice gate if the submarine is not already fitted with one. At other times it can also be used

six times more than the Third Reich had when the second world war began and nearly half of the number employed during the whole war.

Technical description

A conventional third generation submarine can be described as a vessel designed to sail permanently under water, charging its batteries at snorkel depth with the diesel engines and not emerging unless it is for an extremely serious situation, an emergency, or for allowing crew members to embark or disembark.

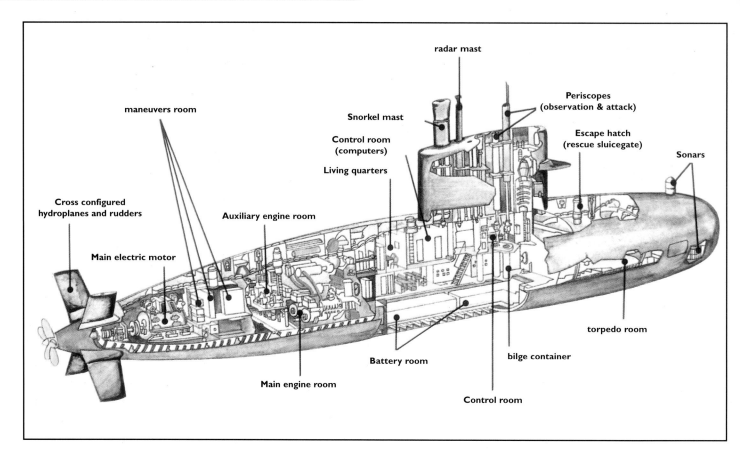

by members of the crew to gain access to the boat when it is undergoing repairs when an opening is blocked by large pieces of equipment being moved through (such as engines parts, batteries etc). In such cases the whole ship is taken apart with all of the services being worked on. This is a job which can last up to a year or more.

Maneuvers

The maneuverability of single propeller submarines in restricted areas such as docks and bases is limited and is a precarious operation should the commander try to do so. This means that the help of auxiliary vessels such as tugs is necessary to complete the operation safely. The modern submarine however, comes into its own when at sea and submerged, were it becomes a highly efficient vessel.

There are usually two steering rudders, one on the upper part of the hull and other on the lower part, as well as two hydroplanes at the stern side which form a type of cross with the rudders. At the bow or on the conning tower there is another pair of hydroplanes, which in most cases fold back into the casing.

Propulsion

The propulsion for these submarines is

INTERIOR

A view of the interior of a modern Walrus class 3rd generation Dutch submarine with part of the hull cut away.

usually a combination of diesel engines powering electrical generators, which in turn supplies electrical current to the main motor. At the same time the diesel engine is also charging the main battery. This is made from almost 400 components; this is the classic type of lead/acid battery with the electrolyte being agitated while it is giving off gas to obtain better performance. The upper part of the connections between the plates and the batteries is cooled with a closed circuit of fresh water. The battery is powerful enough to allow the vessel to be underway for more than one week at its quietest speed.

The main motor is cooled by air, which is cooled by passing it through a water cooled heat exchanger unit. The motor for silent running only allows low speeds to be maintained, but without time limitations. This can either be a separate motor or form part of the main motor, by only using part of the windings.

Weapons and systems

Third generation submarines are armed with torpedos, encapsulated missiles fired from the torpedo tubes and mines. According to the type and mode of operation, two dozen of the

former and double this of the latter can be fired.

The group of sensors which makes up the passive radar and sonar systems (for listening purposes) or the active ones (for attack), are both extremely sensitive and exist in a considerable number of variations including towed and lateral scanning systems.

Performance

A third generation submarine can descend to considerable depths, these typically being 300 meters, which mean a pressure of 30 kg/cm^2, something, which is possible only with special designs. This needs a hull, with the appropriate profiles and sections, which at the same time has

GOTLAND CLASS

The three Gotland class submarines are unique in that they are the only vessels in the world with an AIP system. This system as used by Sweden employs a Stirling motor for main propulsive power, and is capable of delivering 75kw.

GALERNA

The Spanish submarine Galerna, S-71, is coming to the surface in this spectacular shot. The four Galerna class boats are derived from the French Agosta design, together with the four Delphin, they will be replaced by the 4th generation Scorpene/AIP, which are to enter service between 2004 and 2008.

to be built from very strong but flexible steel to allow the hull to bend and deform without cracking and breaking up.

The so-called coefficient of discretion is the relationship between the time in which a submarine can be underway on batteries alone, against the time it has to use its snorkel for air and with the diesel engines working. It is at this moment that it can be detected by infrared systems, which capture the heat of the exhaust gases, or by radar, which detects the reflections against the snorkel head.

The maximum speed of these vessels is around 15-20 knots when submerged and less, between 10 & 12 knots, when on the surface. However, their range when submerged and powered by the diesel engines at snorkel depth, is around 4,000 /6,000 miles at some 6 to 8 knots. However, when on the surface the range is reduced to 2,000/3,000 miles. The so-called prowling speed is approx. 4-6 knots, as this is the most silent speed it is therefore more difficult to be detected by enemy systems.

If it is necessary it can stay permanently and uninterruptedly at sea for close to 20/30 days.

The AIP propulsion system considerably improves the performance of these vessels, so much so that a large increase in their number is expected in the future. However, increasing the range under water has the effect of complicating the design and making it more expensive.

Modern anti-submarine warfare is completely different to what we are normally shown on television or at the cinema. It is dark, quiet work, which can last for days and days with sensors listening for the sound which might identify the existence of a submarine somewhere in the vicinity.

From Asdic to Sonar

The moment in which submersible boats finally became submarines, is the moment when it was no longer necessary to have to surface to both recharge the batteries and/or increase the range, they became completely invisible, except of course for the conventional type of submarines.

The great advantage of a submersible came from being able to attack when under the water, with the normal situation involving a night attack from the surface, this offering much greater mobility. On the surface the submersible was little different from any other surface ship, and could be detected by an attentive look out. With the arrival of radar it could be detected electronically and independently of the light and weather conditions. Initially, they were attacked by the normal

ACOUSTIC TRACKING

The acoustic tracker, as shown in the picture here, is one of the commonly used passive detection methods. It consists of a long plastic tube bristling with ultra-sensitive microphones, which can capture the smallest of sounds.

MILAS

One of the anti-submarine tactics most widely used is the launching of a torpedo on the back of a rocket over long distances as is shown with this MILAS. For this reason the US Navy ASROC (Anti-Submarine Rockets) and the French Malafon missiles were created.

armaments of the day i.e., by gunnery fire, airplanes, bombs, depth charges, etc.

Once submerged the only way of detecting a submarine and monitoring its position is by the use of hydrophones or Asdic equipment (acronym for Anti-Submarine Detection), a word used up to the second world war, but which in modern times is much better known as sonar. In this case the word being an acronym for Sound Navigation And Ranging.

These days passive sonars are spoken of when referring to listening functions and active when acoustic sound waves are sent out and then reflect off a submarine.

Passive sonar

Submarine listening equipment consists of one or a variety of ultra-sensitive microphone assemblies which detect sounds over long distances, at times being spectacularly effective. This greatly depends on a number of aspects, including the quality of the equipment used, but also on the water conditions which can have a lot of influence on the results (temperature, density, salinity etc). It is necessary to know such information beforehand so that the data can be introduced to the computer system, which can then adapt and modify the information received.

Active sonar

As the name suggests active sonar systems does not just listen for sounds, but instead emit their own ultra-sonic impulses which travel through the water until they hit a submerged object. The impulse is then reflected back to its source. Depending on the time it takes to do this and the strength of the returning signal, the range of the object can be precisely calculated. The direction and depth of the submarine can also be ascertained as a result of knowing the orientation and angle of the original emission.

ENEMY FRIGATE

One of the submarine's traditional enemies is the frigate; an escort ship specially equipped to carry out anti-submarine warfare (ASW). This picture shows the Spanish Extremadura, a modified Knox class ship.

DOUBLE BOFORS

Although we are in the era of intelligent ASW weaponry, some traditional concepts still continue being employed, but in more advanced forms, such as these mortar depth charge launchers (the photograph shows a double 375mm bofors).

These days sonar is even used by fishing boats to help locate the schools of fish.

The "boundary layer" effect

The oceans consist of layers of salt water, with significant variations in salinity and temperatures, these layers can vary according to which part of the ocean you are in. The latitude also has a bearing, as does the proximity of warm or cold water currents. There is also a significant variation between the open sea and coastal waters, in which the water density. varies from one area to another. This also

thing which has its greatest effect with water near the surface. From a certain depth, depending on the environmental conditions, its influence is not appreciable. From the 1970's a special sonar model was put into service inside a hydrodynamic vessel commonly referred to as the fish. This is connected to the end of a long cable capable of reaching considerable depths, where submarines cannot remain without being detected.

VDSs (Variable Deep Sonar) are extremely effective in anti-submarine warfare, in addition to sonar buoys and acoustic trackers.

Sonar buoys

When it is believed that a submarine has been detected, the area in question is marked out with a quantity of passive listening buoys, which at the same time house a miniature transmitter emitting the signals captured. In this way a relatively large surface area can be listened to without the need to physically be there at all. These sonar buoys cannot destroy submarines themselves, but they are effective for discovering them.

Acoustic trackers

With the appearance of nuclear submarines with their high speed and mobility it became essential to be able to detect them over great distances, especially with the fact

depends on the time of day, given that the sun's heat is not the same at dawn as it is at mid-day or in the evening.

However, as the conditions for wave propagation and refraction vary considerably depending on these conditions, when a sonar operation is being carried you have to bear in mind that the impulses may not penetrate the various layers. In this way if a submarine knows that it is being looked for, it can use these layers of water as a shield and remain undetected.

.

VDS

The boundary layer phenomenon is some-

BOFOR SHELLS

The shells used by bofors mortars have a range of 3,600m, weigh 250 kg, have close proximity & timer fuses and the warhead carries some 100 kg of high explosive.

THE ASROCs POINT

At the top of this picture you will see the space for ASROCs and the crane with wich the projectiles are loaded onto the launcher via the hatchways high up on the left.

DEPTH CHARGE

The traditional depth charge continues to be used even today, but with various modifications and updates, which in particular refers to the depth it is possible to reach and to the fall speed. In this picture a British Mk-11 (weight of 145 kg, 80 kg of high explosive and 90m depth) is shown along with a Stingray search torpedo.

not unusual to have a total length of around one mile (nearly two kilometers), or even more. The tracker is made up of an assembly of ultra-sensitive microphones inside the tube. In addition, this is filled with a special gel, which helps sound to be received better. This is something similar to the system adopted in an ultra-sound scanner.

Acoustic scanners are very suitable for listening work in oceans where there are huge free areas, however they end up being much less suitable in internal seas or restricted areas, for example in the Mediterranean, the Red Sea and the Persian Gulf. There are also some other technical reasons for this, these being associated with the nuisance caused by the length of the stalker over the ship's stern, making maneuvers difficult.

Attacks from the surface

Although submarine depth charges still exist along with other similar weapons, the most normal situation would be for a submarine to be attacked by acoustic torpedos, using one of the many different types existing at the moment.

These types of torpedos are usually smaller in diameter and size than the ones used by submarines, this requires ships to have special tubes so that these weapons can be launched. Any kind of anti-submarine warfare carried out from the surface will normally involve two different forms of vehicle: the listening ship (destroyer, frigate or corvette) as well as

that such submarines, armed with fast and long range torpedoes, could fire them from long distances and have a reasonable chance of remaining out of the detection zone. Alternatively they could enter and leave important areas without being detected.

Passive sonars continued to reduce in size to the extent that they could be kept inside domes and housings built into the hull of a ship. It became essential that these listening systems could reliably detect a submarine when it was a long distance away.

The solution came about in the form of an acoustic tracker, commonly known as the stalker, which is deployed over the stern side and remains submerged to increase its effectiveness. Trackers such as these are identified by their individual characteristics, such as TACTAS (Tactical Towed Array Sonar) or TACTASS (Tactical Towed Acoustic Sensor System), and they can detect submarines submersed at great depths up to a hundred kilometers away in good environmental conditions. This is normally confidential information.

An acoustic tracker is made up of a large plastic tube, sometimes more than I km long. This is fitted to the end of a towing cable, it

RUSSIAN ASW WEAPONS

The Russian fleet uses different types of ASW armaments from its rocket launchers (which can handle a variety of different types of missiles). In this photograph there is a six unit RBU 1,000 rocket launcher. This can launch shells with 55 kg warheads over distances of 1,000 m.

anti-submarine helicopters, which in the LAMPS versions (Light Airborne Multi-Purpose) communicate via a special link with the base ship. Alternatively the information received by the helicopters sensors can appear simultaneously on the screens on board the ship and vice versa. In this way it is easier to give the final attack order with both craft working from the same accurate information.

Attacking from another submarine

When the attacker is another submarine, detection is made by using the onboard sonar sensors: lateral, towed or hull mounted or alternatively through external help. Although a vessel capable of moving through the kind of water masses that a submarine does is not so subject to finding itself with boundary layer problems.

Once contact has been checked and the attack decided, the submarine can get on with its work by using some of the various anti-submarine torpedos it has available. The great advantage or disadvantage of an action

ENEMY DESTROYER

One of the submarine's traditional adversaries is the destroyer, normally a bigger ship than a frigate and the vessel more geared towards being an escort for the battle fleet. The U.S.S. Moosbrugger, shown here, is one of the 24 vessels making up the Spruance class, and was the last US destroyer built without the AEGIS system, she entered service in 1983.

SONAR

The main component of a submarine attack is active sonar, made up of a large number of transmitter assemblies, the waves hit the target and return to the origin, allowing the position and distance to be discovered. Compare this sonar system's transducer, or active antenna, with the size of the technician working on it.

between two submarines is that both are specialists in this activity, with the hunter becoming the hunted very quickly.

ANTIETAM

In the photo, the *Antietam*, one of the ships of this class, which has medium grade of updating.

The cruiser was, in days gone by, a powerful, heavily armed warship of great importance. Today its main role is to protect aircraft carrier fleets, doing so by providing an electronics umbrella, and the capability to offer a wide range of responses.

The Ticonderogas

When the United States Navy began its massive program to build up a nuclear aircraft carrier fleet, it soon saw that these mammoth vessels required escort ships, which could effectively accompany them without giving rise to any problems of range limitation. The answer came in the form of nuclear cruisers, a ship which the navy had considerable experience of and which, for reasons associated with budgetary problems, only six (of the more than thirty wanted) were built.

The fifteen aircraft carriers and four battleships at the beginning of the 1980s constituted the battle and action group of the US Navy

TICONDEROGA

All of the Ticonderogas have TACTAS sonic tracker launchers located at the stern. In addition, more towards the port side of the ship, there are SLQ-25 Nixies, anti-torpedo decoys.

respectively and required, according to the directives of the time, a minimum of 27 cruisers to protect them. This worked out at a recommended average of 1.5 heavy escort per group.

Initially, it was thought that the Ticonderoga class would be nuclear powered ships, but

OFFENSIVE POWER

A Ticonderoga's greatest offensive power comes from its VLS loaded with missiles of every kind, including its eight anti-ship Harpoon missiles. In the picture we can see a part section of the U.S.S. Leyte Gulf, CG-55, her after deck with Harpoon missiles and 127 mm guns, stern VLS launchers, the flight deck and hanger.

However, they would have to go through a variety of modifications in order to be adapted for the new role. The increase in displacement (close to 18 %) caused a proportional change in the ship's draft, which increased from 8.8m below the sonar dome to 9.5m. This necessitated the mounting of a gunwale along the length of the fo'c'sle up to the 127 mm gun, with the aim of keeping the bow of the ship relatively dry.

Other internal changes limited the armour plating protection of vital spaces such as the storerooms, CIC etc, which use Kevlar. The increase in the amount of electronic equipment (AEGIS, etc) and the array of weapons (VLS launchers) demanded that the power production had to be greater. This meant that gas turbine turbo generators had to be used, which at the same time meant an increase in the fuel capacity to maintain the required range of operation.

War operations

During the Desert Storm and Desert Shield operations against Iraq, these ships took on a great deal of responsibility and some of them came out of it in a bad way. An example of this was the Princeton which was seriously damaged by two magnetic mines, which were probably Italian manufactured, and exploded along her starboard side, close to the propeller shaft

congress would not approve a budget big enough to do so. Finally, these vessels were built following on from an already existing project. This involved the use of conventional propulsion systems, in this case gas turbines. This project was that of the Spruance destroyers, vessels with enough displacement in reserve, space and power to accept the challenge.

SOUTH CAROLINA

Before the Ticonderoga's the US Navy built some nuclear cruisers, but with a reduced number of them due to their high price. This photograph shows the U.S.S. South Carolina, CGN-37, which was delivered in 1975 and is due to be decommissioned in 1999.

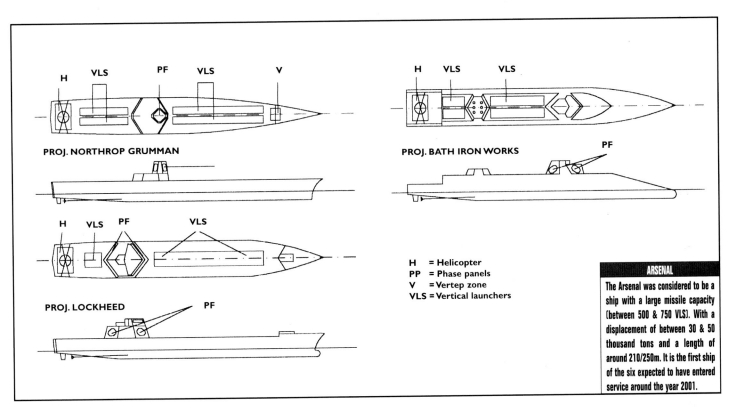

PROJ. NORTHROP GRUMMAN

PROJ. BATH IRON WORKS

PROJ. LOCKHEED

H = Helicopter
PP = Phase panels
V = Vertep zone
VLS = Vertical launchers

ARSENAL

The Arsenal was considered to be a ship with a large missile capacity (between 500 & 750 VLS). With a displacement of between 30 & 50 thousand tons and a length of around 210/250m. It is the first ship of the six expected to have entered service around the year 2001.

and near one of the stabilizer fins. The ship, badly damaged, with the hull deformed and twisted, also suffered serious electrical breakdowns. The starboard engines had been lifted from their seats and were wrecked. Urgent repairs were carried out in Dubai for seven weeks to make her seaworthy for the voyage back to the USA, were she spent a further two months undergoing repairs. The damage was so severe, that consideration was given to withdrawing her from active service.

During this same war against Iraq in 1991 the Ticonderoga's launched a total of 105 SSM Tomahawk missiles (Bunker Hill- 28, Normandy- 26, Mobile Bay- 22, San Jacinto- 14, Philippine Sea- 10, Princeton- 3 and Leyte Gulf- 2). In addition, on the 23rd of June 1993, the Chancellorsville launched another 9 Tomahawks against Iraq in one of the punishment operations against the country.

One of these ships, the U.S.S. Vincennes, also became involved in a serious international incident on the 3rd of July 1988 when it shot down an Iranian commercial Jumbo jet with two missiles. It was said at the time that all of the combat equipment was under automatic control. It appears that the ship's sensors confused this Jumbo for an Iranian F-14 Tomcat believed to be beginning an attack. Without any

LAUNCHERS

The first five ships of the class (*Ticonderoga, Yorktown, Vincennes, Valley Forge & Thomas S. Gates*- the last being the one shown in the picture) are still provided with conventional Mk 26 mod 5 launchers. These are capable of launching SAM Standard missiles and ASROC's (Anti-Submarine Rockets).

further ado the two missiles were fired and the plane shot down. This incident cost the lives of the 290 passengers and the plane's crew.

The Arsenal project

Since the Iraq-Kuwait crisis in 1990 the American Navy has nurtured the idea of having a heavy surface ship capable of launching a large quantity of ground attack missiles, the objective being to get rid of anyone responsible for terrorism. In fact, the idea was of maintaining an operation against anyone responsible for triggering a world crisis, but at the same time in a politically secure way, ensuring

that the lives of ordinary people were not put in danger.

It was said recently that this project has been abandoned because of the high costs which were being incurred, related with the aim of building a cruiser of the future. The ship would be provided with a very much

SUPERSTRUCTURES

The silhouette of the Ticonderoga class is unmistakable as a result of its large superstructure blocks at the bow and stern. These support the SPY phase panels, the heart of the AEGIS system.

COMMAND BRIDGE AND SPY PANEL

This view shows the striking presence of the Command Bridge and SPY panel at the bow/starboard position with 61 VLS bow side missiles housed just below. The 127/54mm gun can be seen between the bow and the launcher.

reduced superstructure, with the weapons and electronics systems contained inside the ship and operating with an extraordinarily reduced crew size (around 50 people). It would also have been capable of being remote controlled from other ships, installations or even by military satellites. The most recent news regarding this has indicated that this project has effectively been thrown out in favor of the new DD-21 or the 21st Century Surface Combatant Ship.

The DD-21

This project emerged at nearly the same time as the Arsenal, but with the difference being that none of its main characteristics have been made available, except that it must incorporate concepts relating to effectiveness, low cost, discretion, modularity, reduced crew numbers and multipurpose capability.

Recently, it has also been given the role of land attack destroyer, something that the Arsenal was also being designated for. As a consequence, given the significant similarities between both of them, as well as the extremely high costs that have been forecast these extremely sophisticated ships are incurring. it appears

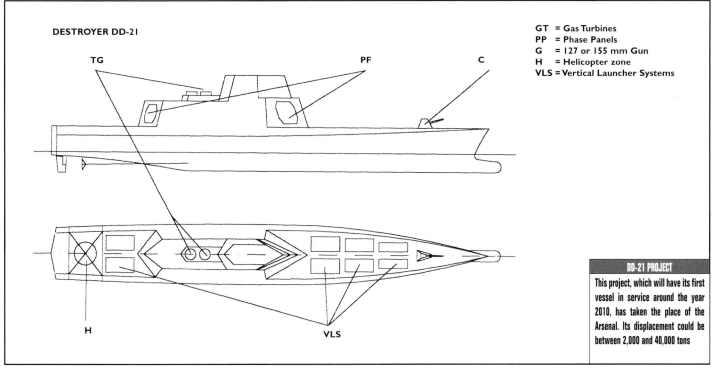

DESTROYER DD-21

TG   PF   C

GT = Gas Turbines
PP = Phase Panels
G   = 127 or 155 mm Gun
H   = Helicopter zone
VLS = Vertical Launcher Systems

H   VLS

DD-21 PROJECT

This project, which will have its first vessel in service around the year 2010, has taken the place of the Arsenal. Its displacement could be between 2,000 and 40,000 tons

likely that one will end up absorbing the other. This is according to the latest information released on the matter CG-47, and Oliver H. Perry, FFG-7, as well as the two Spruance/Kidd destroyer classes, DD-963/DDG-993. It is expected to complement the new CG-21 cruisers or air dominance cruisers, which are defined as multipurpose surface ships, with their primary

ARKANSAS

Initially the Virginia class (the one we can see in the picture is the fourth vessel the U.S.S. Arkansas) was expected to be built in large numbers. There was an estimate of twenty ships. However, after the end of the Vietnam War and with the restrictions imposed, plus the fact that the future of this type of ship was not too clear, the number ended up being cut.

missions concentrating on ground attacks, to be used as such alongside the DDG-51 Arleigh Burke class destroyers.

They will be built under the provisions of Public Law Order 103-160, section 845, whose provisions were previously followed by the DARPA (Defense Advanced Research Projects Agency), for the Arsenal cruiser.

ATTACK AND DEFENCE SHIPS

Ticonderoga class cruisers are medium sized ships, powerfully armed with missiles for anti-ship missions, and also for carrying out ground attacks in punishment or strike back missions. In addition they have excellent anti-aircraft and anti-missile defense capabilities, having been created initially as escorts for aircraft carrier fleets.

The purchase programme was structured into five phases. Phase one, the design concept was expected to cost a total of 6 million dollars. This phase finished on the 1st of April 1998, at which point the corresponding contracts were to be awarded.

Phase two, the initial system design, led to the selection of two of the contractors, which bid in the first phase: Bath Iron Works/Lockheed Martin GES and Ingalls Shipbuilding/Raytheon Systems. It was forecast that the costs would not exceed 45 million dollars (15 from the 1999 budget and 30 from the year 2000), that it would last 24 months and with estimates that contracts would be awarded at the beginning of 1999.

Phase three, the main system and the design of the sub-system completed. The number of contractors was to be reduced to only one. This would last approximately another 24 months and it was estimated that the contract would be awarded around January 2001.

Phase four, details for the design and construction of the lead ship of the series, with a forecast of 60 months to do so. The estimated cost is 750 million dollars per ship, with the delivery of the first one taking place in the

SHILOH

In this view of one of the latest Ticonderoga's, the U.S.S. Shiloh, the large IR filters for the gas turbine exhausts can be seen out. These reduce the infrared signature. We can also clearly see the CIWS Vulcan Phalanx on the port side.

year 2008. The complete program was for an expected 32 ships to be built in a ten year period.

Phase five refers to the lifespan of the ship with the estimate being that each DD-21 would have an active military life of 35 years.

The Russian Navy ("Rosiyskiy Voen-nomorsky Flot") is the only one at the present time which still maintains large surface ships in service with the objective of destroying enemy surface ships, especially aircraft carriers.

Anti-Aircraft Carrier Strategies

The death of the dictator Stalin in March 1953, as well as the arrival in service of large American attack aircraft carriers halfway through the 1950's brought about a change in Soviet naval strategy and philosophy. This fact and its implications were intensified with the availability of the first true SSM anti-ship missiles with their fearsome military capability, the SS-N-2 Styx, used in hundreds of fast missile launches from the Komar class of ships (built between 1959 & 1961) and the Osa class (1961-1966).

The consequences of this became evident in dramatic fashion when in October 1967 the Israeli destroyer Eilat was sunk by one of the Russian Komar missiles sent to Egypt. Another important incident, but less well known was the first shooting down of an anti-ship missile by an anti-missile missile. This took place in Vietnam in April 1972 when a SAM Terrier fired

SLAVA

The Slavia class cruisers are smaller in size and military more importance than the Kirov class, but should not be underestimated as adversaries. They are very new, with the fourth of the series still to enter service and expected to do so in 1999.

DOUBLE BANK

The hidden double bank of SAM SA-N-4 missiles has direct access to the magazine of 20 missiles, in 4 rotating loaders of 5 units, positioned underneath it.

from the U.S.S. Sterett DLG-31, a American destroyer, hit and blew up a SS-N-2 Styx which had been launched by a North Vietnamese Komar unit.

The latent danger represented by the SS-N-2 missile increased after the arrival in service of the SS-N-3 Shaddock. This was mounted on the Raketny Kreyser (missile cruiser) of the Kynda class, the first Soviet ship designed in such a way with its eight SSM missiles and entering service in June 1962..

KIROV

The Kirov class (the Piotr Veliky is shown here, the fourth in the series) are large cruisers with weaponry designed to attack surface ships thanks to its twenty SSM SS-N-19 Shipwreck supersonic missiles (Mach 1.6) with a range of up to 450 km and active radar guidance. Its warhead can be high explosive (750kg) or nuclear (350kT).

Anti-submarine strategy

In parallel the US Navy put its Polaris armed submarine fleet into service, presenting the most serious threat yet, with its missiles aimed straight at the heart of the USSR. As a result the navy's strategic and tactical planners had to come up with ways of dealing with two dangers simultaneously. In other words to counteract the aircraft carrier task forces and the SLBM Polaris missiles on board strategic submarines.

Initially Russia designed and constructed Moskva class hybrids called Protivolodochny Kreyser (anti-submarine cruisers) which had flight decks allowing the ships to operate with up to 14 ASW Ka-25 Hormone helicopters. In addition there were some ships following the lines of Western helicopter carrier cruisers such as the Italian Andrea Doria and Vittorio Veneto and French Jeanne D'Arc. There were successive classes of ships entering service without multipurpose weaponry, given that they often leaned, towards one type of threat or another. The Kiev entered service in May 1976, the first ship of its class, having SS-N-12

ANTI-AIRCRAFT MOUNTS

The CADS-N-1 anti-aircraft/missile mount is a mixture of artillery and missile weaponry. It consists of two 30mm guns and two groups each with four encapsulated missile launchers. These are not mounted in the unit shown in the photograph, this version being known as the SA-N-11. This is a naval variety of the army's SA-18A (photograph below).

Sandbox anti submarine weaponry (ASuW) with possible nuclear warheads. In addition it had Ka-25 Hormone helicopters at the same time as it was operating with Yak-38 STOVL Forger aircraft and included a powerful array of anti-aircraft and anti-missile weapons, these consisting of SA-N-4 missiles and AK-630 anti-missile guns.

CHARACTERISTICS

SHIP	KIROV (2)	SLAVA (4)
YEAR DELIVERED	1988/1995	1982/1999
DIMENSIONS	252 x 28 x 9.1	186 x 21 x 7.6
DISPLAC.	24.300	11.200
PROPULSION	CONAS	COGAG/COGOG
ENGINES	GT3A-688 Turbines	Gas Turbines (4+2)
POWER	140,000	125,000
SPEED/RANGE	30-14,000/30	32-7,500/15
WEAPONRY	20 SSM SS-N-19 missiles	16 SS-N-12 SSM missiles
	40 SA-N-4 SAM missiles	64 SA-N-6 SAM missiles
	6 SA-N-6 SAM missiles	40 SA-N-4 SAM missiles
	128 SA-N-9 SAM missiles	2 (I x II) 130/70 mm guns
	96 CADS-N1 missiles/guns	6 CIWS AK 650 sextuplets
	SS-N-15 ASW missiles	10 (2 x V) 533 mm LT tubes
	2 (I x II) 130/70 mm guns	2 RBU 6000 (2 x XII) ASW mortars
	10 (2 x V) 533 mm LT tubes	
	1 RBU 12000 (I x X) ASW mortar	
	2 RBU 1000 (2 x VI) ASW mortars	

The latest Russian cruisers

In July 1980 a large cruiser called the Kirov was delivered to the Soviet fleet. This was considered as the flagship of its class, an enormous nuclear powered vessel. These were the first surface nuclear ships in the Soviet/Russian fleet to have a displacement and size comparable with the battleships and cruisers of the Second World War. The three other vessels of the class entered service in 1983 *(Frunze)*, 1988 *(Kalinin)* and 1995 *(Pyotr Velikiy, the ex Yuri Andropov)*. This class is officially known as the "Raketny Kreyser", Missile Cruiser.

Meanwhile, the deliveries of other ships, part of another class of vessel, were interspersed with those of the Kirov. These were the Slavas which should have amounted to five ships: the *Slava, Marshal Ustinov, Chevrona Ukraina, Admiral Lobov* and the last and fifth vessel which was cancelled in October 1990. The official classification is the same as the other, the "Raketny Kreysner", Missile Cruiser.

A variety of ships saw their operational life altered by the political changes, which took place in the old Soviet Union, at the beginning of the 1990's. Names were also changed during this period, at the same time as others were being taken out of service as a result of the maintenance problems they presented.

Of the four Kirovs, only two are in active service at the moment, the *Pyotr Velikiy* (ex *Yuri Andropov*) and *Admiral Nakhimov* (ex *Kalinin*). The other two, the *Admiral Ushakov* (ex *Kirov*) and *Admiral Lazarev* (ex *Frunze*) remain in reserve, assigned to the North and Pacific fleets respectively.

The Slava class also had their names changed to those being used at the moment, the *Moskva*, ex *Slava*; *Marshal Ustinov*; *Varyag*, ex *Chernova Ukraina* and the *Admiral Lobov*, ex *Ukraina*. This last ship is being completed at a slow pace and will be delivered to the Russian fleet in 1999. It has been the object of some negotiations between The Russian and Ukrainian governments, with the Nikolaiev Nord shipyards, where it is being built, being on the banks of the Black Sea, in the Ukraine, which is now an independent republic.

It was on board the Slava, off Malta in 1989, that the meeting of the two most powerful men in the world took place. They were the Presidents of the USA and USSR, George Bush and Mikhail Gorbachov.

The Kirovs

These large cruisers, with the exception of aircraft carriers, are the biggest warships built since the Second World war. They are propelled by a Combined Nuclear and Steam system, this being a system where pressurised water reac-

---

FO'C'SLE

Although the Kirov's fo'c'sle appears relatively clear of equipment and weaponry, the reality is different. Just below each of the small lateral superstructures, which house the AK-650 mounts there are also 20 VLS's for SSM missiles. In front of these there are 12 VLS units with eight launchers for SAM SA-N-6 missiles.

tors generate steam, which is then reheated by conventional boilers fuelled by diesel fuel. This is a propulsion system which, up to now, has not been repeated in any other ship. With their GT3A-688 turbines delivering a total of 140,000 horsepower and their two variable pitch propellers, they are capable of reaching speeds up to 32 knots on a full load of 24,300 tons. These cruisers have a range is 14,000 miles at 30 knots and are the result of project number 1,144 of Severnoe's design office.

They have a solid, powerful silhouette and considerable differences between the ships can be noticed. This is as a result of applying changes to the follow-on vessels, with some lessons having been learned from previous experiences. This means the features are not homogenous across all of the ships, and there are various detail differences between each ship.

The military power of these ships is based on twenty supersonic ASuW Chelomney SS-N-19 Shipwreck missiles (Mach 1.6) which can be fitted with nuclear warheads, and they have a low flight trajectory profile (sea-skimmers). These are basically a modification of SS-12-N missiles, contained in vertical launch silos on the fo'c'sle. In front of these there are twelve vertical launch silos each with eight launchers. These are for SAM SA-N-6 (Grumble) air defense missiles,

THE KIROVS IN SERVICE

The construction of the *Admiral Nahkimov* (ex *Kalinin*) began in 1983, and she entered service in 1988. Along with the Piotr Veliky, these are the only two Kirovs remaining in service. These four ships should be considered as having evolved from the same design, bearing in mind that each has considerable differences in appearance from the others.

forming a part of the AEGIS type defense system. These are also supersonic (Mach 2,8), and with the possibility of carrying nuclear warheads. The SAM missile group is further complemented by two hidden banks of 40 SA-N-4 Geko missiles for defense work with a speed of Mach 2.5 and also by 128 SA-N-9 Gauntlet missiles. The array of missiles is completed by six mounts, which are a combination of 8 missiles/2 CADS-N-1 30mm guns and ASW Starfish SS-N-15 missiles. Each of the latter with the corresponding 40 type torpedoes, with conventional or nuclear warheads. The ASW weaponry is completed with three

ELECTRONICS

The Slava's electronics are important with a three dimensional Top Pair radar at the stern, with the aim of carrying out air searches and looking for targets of particular dimensions over a distance of 366 km. For air and surface searches there is the 3-D Top Steer radar high above the bridge.

RADAR SYSTEMS

Just in front of the bridge is the Front Door system, which is used for fire control (for SS-N-12 missiles); above the Command Bridge is the Kite Screech system for controlling the 130/70mm guns. The domes in front of the bridge are for the Bass Tilt equipment, which controls the AK 650 anti-missile system, tearing into the sky when fired.

mortars, two RBU 1000s and one RBU 12000.

With respect to other traditional conventional armaments, this consists of two 130mm guns in a single turret and two CIWS AK-630 mounts.

They also have ten 533mm torpedo launchers in two mounts, with the possibility of being able to use different types of torpedo as well as SS-N-15 missiles. The electronic equipment systems consist of 3-D Top Pair air search radar; Top Plate air/surface search radar; Palm Frond for navigation; Cross Sword, Top Dome, Tomb Ste, Pop Ground turning control; Kite Screech & Hot

RUSSIAN GUNS

Russian artillery/guns have always enjoyed an excellent reputation. They are considered to be the most efficient and toughest of weapons. This 130/70 mm automatic twin barrelled gun turret has a range of 29 km and a rate of fire per barrel of 45 rounds per minute. Each shell has a weight of 33.4 kg, the elevation ranges between +85 to -15 degrees and a muzzle velocity of 1,000 meters per second. It entered service in 1981 (photograph below)

Flash; Flyscreen B Air Control; IFF Salt Pod A, B & Tacan Round House; Tin Man, Punch Bowl SATCOM weapon control; Low Ball SATNAV, Bell Crown datalink and Bell Push. Also incorporated is the Horse Jaw hull mounted sonar system; VDS Horse Tail; Foot Ball ESM/ECM electronic warfare system; Weine Flask; Bell Bash; Bell Nip; Half Cup; countermeasure decoys; 150mm PK2 buoy launchers; and tracking torpedoes.

The Slavas

These are conventional ships powered by six gas turbines driving two propellers. The COGAG system is used, 2 turbines for normal cruising, the other four are used when maximum power is required. The maximum power delivered by these engines is 108,000 horsepower, giving a maximum speed of 32 knots and a range of 2,500 miles at 30 knots, or 15,000 miles at 7.5 knots. They have a displacement when fully loaded, of 11,200 tons. In addition they are powerfully armed with SSM/ASuW SS-N-12, SAM/AAW SA-N-6, SA-N-4 missiles and ASW RBU-6000 anti-submarine rocket launchers. It has a 130/70 mm AK130 twin barrelled turret and six CIWS AK 650 mounts.

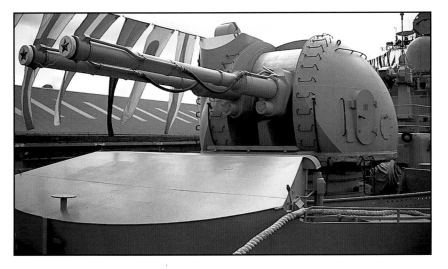

US Navy task forces have entrusted their anti-missile, anti-aircraft and anti-submarine defense to Ticonderoga, CG-47 class cruisers, and to Arleigh Burke, DDG-51 class destroyers. These are multipurpose ships, all of which are provided with the AEGIS combat system.

The AEGIS shield

The AEGIS combat system which has been given the name of Perseus' shield, immediately detects any aerial or maritime object within a radius of 200 miles, even something the size of a bumblebee can be detected. It is capable of simultaneously detecting and following hundreds of different echoes. Once the analyzed contacts have been checked by the IFF (Identification Friend or Foe) system each possible enemy echo is assigned a special danger level, this being based on the data regarding the speed, position, distance etc.

The data is presented to the captain on multiple screens in real time and scale, and at the moment of decision it is he who decides if the counter attack is to be carried out manually or automatically. An AEGIS system is mainly made up

COUNTRIES WITH AEGIS

Until now, apart from the USA, the only other country in the world with ships using AEGIS is Japan (in the photograph we can see the Japanese Kirishina). Russia has a similar system known as Sky Watch.

CIC

The captain controls the whole ship from the CIC, at the same time as receiving information from the range of different systems.

of phased array radar's or fixed SPY panels, UYK computer equipment and VLS missile launchers.

Phased array radar systems

Conventional radar rotates at a predetermined number of turns per minute, and moves correspondingly faster as the echo gets closer and closer. However, because the speed of rotation cannot be increased beyond a certain point (for example when faced with threats covering 5 km in only 10 seconds), ships are equipped

with fixed radar's where the emission and reception of signals is constantly updated and transferred to optical outputs on large data screens. These fixed multiple panels are positioned in four different points on the ship, and in such a way that they cover the 360 degrees of the horizon. They are also located in high positions to give the widest coverage possible.

The SPY-1 phased array panels are made up of multi-function radar and are the heart of the AEGIS system. This is a combined azimuth- horizontal search radar which carries out target acquisition, classification and tracking functions. In addition it can perform a missile guidance role. It operates in the S meter band, between 2,000 and 4,000 MHz. Its wide and almost unlimited capability for detecting and tracking is in practice constrained by the volume of data the computer systems can process. It is difficult for it to be able to manage more than a few hundred contacts at the same time. Its missile guidance capability, bearing in mind the demands of SPG-62

EQUIPMENT
The Arleigh Burke class are equipped with SPY-1D panels instead of the SPY-1As, these being more modern combat systems than the latter.

support, is somewhere around the number of 20 simultaneously.

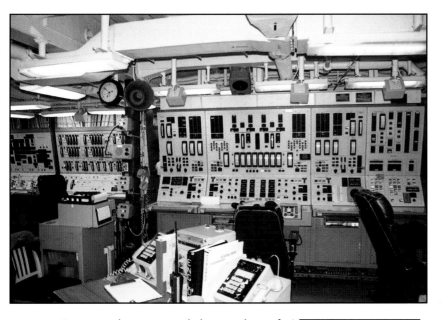

CONTROL
Propulsion control on board an AEGIS ship is centralized in one control room (which at the same time is the internal damage control center).

Detectors

Being a target detection radar, the AEGIS system uses the Raytheon AN-SPG-62 Mk 99, a slave radar for the phased array SPY panels, which is a particularly appropriate system for the SM-2 Standard missile. It works in the X meter band, between 8 and 12,000 MHz.

The Ticonderoga's have four of these radar's, as opposed to the Arleigh Burke class, which only have three.

UYK Computers

These very important computers have the responsibility for carrying out analyses of each individual threat and comparing it with the others. This is done in such a way that the danger of any echo picked up is assessed in accordance with a variety of different parameters.

These computers have a large capacity and processing speed and are capable of carrying out several million operations per second. This allows them to calculate and estimate the different possibilities of success for each attack. Once the final result of this process is obtained and a conclusion made, and depending on the different options available, the system can automatically set the ship's attack in motion and order the firing of the appropriate weapons.

When the first Ticonderoga was delivered the combat equipment configuration was called Baseline 0, employing systems such as SPY-1A panels; twin Mk-26 missile launching banks (with SM-1, SM-2 & ASROC missiles); AN/UYK-7 computers, Mk-1 AEGIS panels and a LAMPS-1 helicopter. The latest equipment models fitted on the Ticonderoga's are referred to as Baseline 4, which have also been fitted to the first Arleigh Burke class destroyers. Baseline 5 refers to the equipment being fitted on these ships at the moment (DDG-57 to

78). This will be followed by Baseline 6 incorporating phased array SPY-1 D(V) panels, TBMD (Theatre Ballistic Missile Defence), ATWCS (Advanced Tomahawk Weapon Control System), AN/UYQ-70 optical panels and ESSM missiles. These will be fitted on the DDG Flight IIAs (from the DDG-79 to the 92). Baseline 7, which is still under construction will incorporate many updates, especially with regards to the computers, which in the future will change from the AN/UYK-44 to the future COTS (Commercial Off The Shelf).

As a comparative indicator of the power of old and later computer systems, the Baseline 0 program consisted of 820,000 lies/instructions whereas the newer Baseline five had 6.5 million.

VLS Launchers

The classic type of the past was a rotary, twin missile bank; this being loaded by complicated mechanisms. This system is a slow one and as a result is not effective against high concentration simultaneous attack. As a result of this, multiple pod systems were designed housing different types of missiles in a variety of configurations. These can be fired simultaneously now that present day missile technology has given missiles the possibility of being guided effectively and, for a brief moment, the possibility of designating its target.

As a general rule, the inside of VLS-41 cells contains Harpoon anti-ship missiles, ASROC anti-submarine missiles, and anti-aircraft/anti-missile missiles. They are also expected to

THE TICONDEROGA'S ORIGINS

The Ticonderoga class were built from the hull design for the Spruance destroyer, but with some specific changes carried out.

CIC

The traditional command post during battle, the bridge, has without doubt had its place taken by the CIC.

include the new ESSM (Evolved Sea Sparrow Missile) and Aster 15 & 30.

Ticonderoga cruisers

This series of ships was built between 1983 and 1994, and at first it was thought that they would be propelled by steam turbines with steam being provided by nuclear reactors. However, the high cost of this system meant that they had to be equipped with conventional propulsion systems consisting of four gas turbines. Because of this, the design for the Spruance DD-963 class of destroyers was modified, this ship becoming the SCB 226. These ships were originally considered to be missile destroyers (DDG) and as a result, had to be reclassified as missile cruisers (CG) before entering service.

During the so-called 100 hours war against Iraq (Operations Desert Storm & Desert Shield) these were the first ships to use Tomahawk missiles in bombing missions against ground targets.

These are the first US Navy ships to widely use the AEGIS combat system (earlier trials were carried out by the aircraft carrier U.S.S. *Enterprise* and the cruiser U.S.S. *Long Beach*,

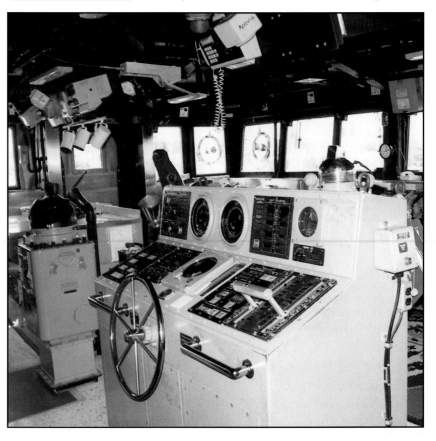

TICONDEROGA CLASS

Ticonderoga class AEGIS cruisers often visit ports in friendly countries. Because they are not nuclear powered this does not cause any problems.

both nuclear powered), this giving them a large and special silhouette. They have cooling filters for the exhaust gasses to reduce the infra-red signature and also the Prairie system to do a similar job for the acoustic signature (the Prairie system produces air bubbles to mask the sounds generated by the ship).

As a result of the greater electrical power needs the original design had to be modified to allow the ships to be changed from 2,000 kW diesel generators to 2,500 kW gas turbine generators. At the same time an increase in the demand for fuel also brought about increases in the displacement and variations in the ships stability.

The Arleigh A. Burke destroyers

These missile destroyers (DDG's) were designed and built as replacements for the Charles F. Adams & Coontz classes. The latter were the first ships in the US Navy to be genuinely built as missile destroyers, and were taken out of service during the 1980s and the beginning of the 1990s.

ARLEIGH A. BURKE

Other US Navy AEGIS ships are the Arleigh A. Burke class destroyers, which entered service from 1991 and of which 28 ships will be built. The Flight II & IIA versions will follow these from the year 2000. In total around eighteen of these ships are expected (photograph below).

Originally it was expected that a total of 49 Arleigh A. Burke class destroyers would be constructed (during the Carter administration), this being increased to 63 during Reagan's Presidency. Finally the high cost of these ships (close to 1,000 million dollars/vessel) reduced expectations and left the number at a total of 28 in the versions Flight I & II plus another 14 of the version Flight IIA.

SPECIAL RADAR

The IFF (Identification Friend or Foe) UPX-29 system is special radar, which identifies as many echoes as come within its range. It can be identified by the characteristic crown high up on the after mast. The highest radar dish is the TACAN or assistance radio beacon for aircraft.

RADAR

The SPS-49 aerial search radar has a range of up to 250 miles (some 450km), and is capable of detecting just about any kind of flying object, no matter how small it may be.

FILTERS

The noticeable and efficient filters positioned at the gas outlets perform a cooling operation for those gases coming hot from the turbines. The result of this is a considerable reduction in the IR signature of these ships.

GUNS

Immediate defense against attacking missiles is assigned to Vulcan Phalanx Mk 15 guns with six 20/76mm barrels, which with their high rate of fire destroy missiles in their last phase of flight.

ELECTRONIC WARFARE SYSTEMS

Electronic warfare systems have the responsibility for detecting any kind of electronic emission from the adversary, later to absorb and disfigure it, as well as nullifying the emission in such a way that the possible enemy ends up being electronically "blind".

PHASED ARRAY SPY-1 MISSILES

Phased array SPY-1 panels are the most valuable components in the whole ship. They have multiple possibilities for detection, selection, tracking and missile guidance both against the enemy and for using its own weapons. Here we can see the outside face of this panel.

MISSILE DETECTORS

SPG-62 Mk 99 designators are the systems, which together with the SPY panels, direct SAM Standard missiles.

MISSILE MOUNTS

Harpoon anti-ship missiles are positioned on the after deck in two missile mounts with four launchers as shown in the photograph. Each missile has a range of up to 160 km, with a tracking warhead loaded with 227 kg of high explosive.

AEGIS CRUISERS

AEGIS cruisers with their wide range of possibilities for detecting objects of negligible size over a radius of hundreds of kilometers, make up the defensive shield for attack aircraft carrier fleets.

MISSILES

The missile component of these ships is based around its two VLS batteries, each of these with 61 cells suitable for firing SSM Tomahawk and SAM missiles of almost all the most normal types.

WEAPONS

Although the main role of these ships will be to support the incomparable electronic systems, this should not mean that we should ignore the weapons available, including the most conventional, such as this 127/54mm Mk 45 gun which fires 32kg shells.

For centuries maritime propulsion came from wind and sail. It is only in the last 250 years that this has been superseded by the irresistible force of steam. But in recent years a great variety of alternative propulsion systems have been brought to the military navies around the world, these always being at the forefront of new technology.

The ship's engine

There is no doubt that the propulsion system is one of the most important components on board modern warships. Clearly slow moving vessels which didn't have the capability of controlling their movements independently would be perfect targets for an enemy. In the not so distant past, around the beginning of the Second World War, it was considered that speed and maneuverability were probably the best defenses that any warship could have. As a result ships were constructed which sacrificed just about anything to improve their performance with respect to speed.

With radar controlled aiming and firing as well as the appearance of missiles, speed has lost a great deal of the importance given to it in the past, but it still continues to be one of the basic performance characteristics which comes up in construction contracts. A ship with a reduced speed capability is still something which is not welcomed with any degree of satisfaction.

STEAM PROPULSION

The American Knox class frigates (the ship in the photograph is a modified Knox built in Spain and in service with the Spanish fleet - the F-75 Extremadura) are without doubt the longest serving warships ships being used at the moment, using steam propulsion. They use superheated steam at 510 degrees at a pressure of 84.4 kg/cm2.

ENGINE

The diesel engine, because of its high earning capacity, is the gas turbine's great competitor, although it cannot be compared with respect to speed or power. This picture shows a Paxman 12VP185 diesel engine, from Alstom.

Steam

To find the first example of steam being used as a propulsion system for boats it is necessary to go all the way back to 1707, to Kassel. Here Denis Papin first dabbled with this type of propulsion system, although the first true practical application did not appear until nearly a century later in 1801.

During almost all of the 19th century the reciprocating steam engine propelled an enormous numbers of ships, ploughing through the seas until 1894, when the Turbinia became the first vessel to be successfully powered by steam turbines. However, it was not until the beginning of the twentieth century when effective and reliable gear systems became available that the steam turbine gained superiority over the steam reciprocating engine.

These days, although steam does not have the importance that it once had, there are still many ships continuing to use the steam turbine.

As a part of all of this it should be noted that when nuclear energy is being used it does not involve the steam boiler which works with fossil fuel (coal or petroleum derivatives) by a nuclear reactor.

The electric engine

The use of the electric motor as a propulsion system for ships had not been seriously considered until the arrival of the submarine. It was a Spaniard, Isaac Peral, who applied it for the first time to such vessels. This development with submarines took place in 1989, at least in a way which is widely recognized.

At the moment new military applications are giving the electric engine considerable importance.

The diesel engine

The first diesel engine fitted on board El Petit in 1902, this was a boat that worked on the French canals.

The diesel engine has been of great importance to maritime propulsion. In the past these engines allowed great feats to be carried out, for example, with submarines during the Second World War. Improvements made to steam engines were taken and used in these engines to improve their performance. They are now the most widely used engines at sea.

GENERAL ELECTRIC GAS TURBINE

The world market for gas turbines is largely dominated by the GE (General Electric) LM2500engine, of which a large central section can be seen here in this external view. However, other gas turbines manufactured in other parts of the world should also be taken into consideration, such as those from Russia and the British Rolls Royce.

The gas turbine

Although in the mechanical world this type of engine had been experimented with before the internal combustion engine came along, it was not until 1947 that an engine of this type was fitted in a ship, when one of the Royal Navys wartime steam gunboats was converted and renamed HGB-2009. Since then it has been greatly improved and at the moment is one the most common propulsion systems on fast warships. The versatility, its start up speed and the rapid acceleration make it an extremely difficult engine to substitute in all the different types of escort ships using it, (such as destroyers, frigates etc).

A COMPARISON OF CHARACTERISTICS, SYSTEMS & TYPICAL ACRONYMS

PURE OR DIRECT		
DIESEL	Diesel engine	Diesel engine coupled with the propeller
ELECTRIC	Generator + engine	The electric propulsion receives current from the battery generator
CONV. STEAM	Steam + turbine	The boiler generates superheated steam, which is used in the turbine
NUCLEAR STEAM	Reactor + turbine	The reactor heats water at pressure inside a closed primary loop. This steam generates steam in another circuit (secondary & open) which is used by the turbine.
MULTIPLE OR COMBINED		
CODAG	Combined diesel & gas	Diesel engine for cruising + gas turbine for maximum speed
CODLAG	Combined diesel,	The electric propulsion engine receives current from the diesel generator group
		Electric & gasor the gas turbine.
CODOG	Combined diesel or gas	Diesel engine for cruising or gas turbine for maximum speed.
COEOG	See CODLAG	
COGAG	Combined gas + gas	Gas turbine for cruising + other for maximum speed.
COGAG (WR21) ICR	Heat exchanger +	One gas turbine with a heat exchanger and heat Recuperator
COGAS	Combined gas & steam	The gas turbine has a heater placed in the gas outlet which generates steam for use in a conventional turbine.
COGOG	Combined gas or gas	Gas turbine for cruising or gas turbine for maximum speed.
CONAS	Combined nuclear or steam	Nuclear reactor superheating steam in a conventional boiler.

NOTE: All of these systems incorporate some type of reducing gearbox and/or variable pitch propellers.

Hybrid Assemblies

It is a fact that one propulsion system can offer specific advantages over other systems, but at the same time also pose some problems. In the case of warships this can very often mean the difference between life and death or the difference between defeating an enemy or being defeated- this being something which is established along very subtle lines. As a result different types of propulsion systems are mixed meaning

STEAM POWER
Ships such as this Norwegian frigate, the Trondheim, using conventional steam power are probably the last few to exist with this kind of power system.

HIGH CONSUMPTION OF STEAM
Two boilers such as this using conventional fuel (Combustion Engineering V2M) supply enough steam (at 510 degrees & 84.4 kg/cm2) for only one steam turbine.

that the best one for the situation can be used at the appropriate time.

The so-called hybrid assemblies incorporate different types of engine in the one group, such as a gas turbine & diesel engine configuration where one or the other can be used depending on the situation. There are almost as many combinations possible as there are types of propulsion. For example, it could be appropriate to use a gas turbine for maximum speed, at the same time as choosing a diesel engine for its economical fuel consumption, or for cruising and maneuverability in a port. However, there are also cases in which a gas turbine is employed for cruising, and the other more powerful system is coupled only when full power is required.

Essential power

One of the most significant differences between a modern warship and one from, for example, a century ago (in addition to the clearly visible ones), is, as is generally well known, the much greater capacity for generating electricity. It is obvious that in ships from the end of the last century there were a number of

adequate margin in this area (together with spare space and/or displacement). This is to prevent the situation where, for example, the use of a future weapon would lower the supply level and seriously deplete the ship's effectiveness.

As a clearer example of this at the moment, the use of laser weapons is just beginning to be talked about. The so-called HELs (High Energy Laser) which would require equipment that could produce enough power, for a short burst of laser energy, Also being very seriously thought about is the use of electrical propulsion systems. Therefore different possibilities of using the electrical energy (always a limited source) generated on board are being considered- for HEL or propulsion, depending on the situation.

specific electricity requirements, mainly to supply different electrical motors and lighting. But the electricity needs were not much more than that.

In most modern ships the production of electrical energy is a necessity which obligates and often leads to the construction of ships with an

CONTROL PANELS

These picture shows the control panel for a gas turbine and, regardless of the power, is extremely complex.

With more advantages

Integral electric propulsion offers even greater advantages with respect to the internal distribution of the ship. Conventional mechanical propulsion systems mean that different parts have to be located in particular points inside the ship, with shafts having to follow certain lines

CODOG PROPULSION

Propulsion of the German frigate F-215 Brandenburg, the lead ship of its class has a CODOG propulsion system, this comprises of two 7LM2500SA-ML gas turbines (51,000 horsepower) and two MTU 20V 956 TB92 (11,070) diesel engines. It has a maximum speed of 29 knots and 18 with diesel alone. The range is 4,000 miles at 18 knots.

and gear boxes & engine units following suit. In an integral electric propulsion system the different parts of the power unit can be positioned where they best fit in with the ship's other necessities, like its acoustic signature, or in accordance with specific project characteristics (e.g. centring, stabilizing features). Hard mechanical links between the generators and engines will not exist, instead there will only be cabling to carry the power.

New Engines

New space technology has allowed the development of a type of electric motor with revolutionary features. This supplies more power than a conventional motor while at the same time being smaller and therefore requiring less space. In addition the characteristics associated with having greater torque are such

WESTHINGHOUSE

The Westinghouse steam turbine used to power Knox class frigates delivers a total of 35,000 horsepower. With this kind of power it can propel these ships (4,200 tons when fully loaded, 134m long and with a 14 m beam) at close to 40 miles per hour (some 54 km/hour).

HIGH ACCELERATION

Gas turbine propulsion allows the engine to go from cold to full power in only 90 seconds, and with acceleration never seen in the maritime world before. In this picture we can see the Dutch frigate (CODOG) heeling over to port after a high speed turn (photograph below).

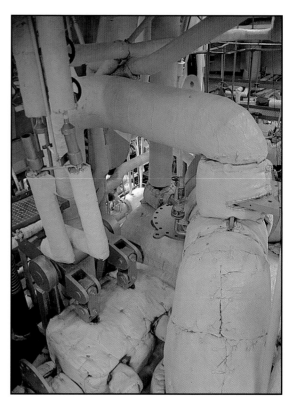

that it will be possible to use heavier propellers which turn more slowly, with the result that they are much more silent. Although at the moment the application possibilities for these motors are expected to be limited to new types of submarines. There is no doubt that with such a wealth of advantages they will end up being used in surface ships, or at least in very specific types of vessels, such as the SWATH. Because of the SWATH's characteristics and unusual shape the engines need to be installed inside large cylinders, which are located below the water, just at the lower edge of the hull sides. This is a position, which considerably complicates the installation of conventional diesel engines or gas turbines. The different aspects associated with the exhaust gases and air intakes also have to be considered.

Cryogenic cooling

With such mechanically delicate systems the use of cryogenically cooled engines has been considered, using refrigeration gases such as liquid Helium or Nitrogen. These allow the adequate cooling of continual current conventional electric motors. It could be done much better with new permanent magnets which can be cooled with closed loop water circuits incorporating a heat exchanger (see 4th Generation Conventional Submarines).

anti-missile components, especially since the appearance of the powerful sea-skimmer missiles.

Low flying

The first missiles had a curved trajectory, being raised for their launch and then following a parabolic profile before reaching a uniform acceleration and linearly increasing speed towards the target. These types of missiles could be detected with a fair amount of ease by the radar systems of the time, given that they climbed from over the horizon, cutting a path across the sky.

The appearance of modern low trajectory missiles meant that they would only climb in altitude in the last phase of flight, by which time there was practically no other solution except to pray. Radar's used on warships became more and more obsolete against these missiles, as they speed towards their targets at very low altitudes, their echoes confused amongst the false ones normally produced by the sea surface.

Radar waves do not adapt to the earth's curvature. Because of this radar is much more effective when it is installed at high points. As a result there are spy satellites, AWACS (Airborne Warning And Control System) aircraft and early warning helicopters (EW).

The present day missile threat, which is becoming more and more sophisticated, has driven the continual modernization of detection systems found on ships.

The missile threat

On the 21st of October 1967, four months after the end of the third Arab-Israeli war, two Russian missiles were fired from an Egyptian patrol boat sank an Israeli destroyer. Since this action missiles have been considered a palpable threat.

However, in the three decades since this happened, missile technology has advanced considerably and the missiles of today have little in common with those SS-N-2 Styx which caused such a stir.

Today warships incorporate the latest in

> **ANTI-SHIP MISSILES**
> One of the first Western anti-ship missiles was the American Harpoon, going into service in the early 1970s. We can see a launching from a American Knox class ASROC (photograph above).

> **EIGHT LAUNCHER MODULES**
> The Mk41 module (incorporating eight launchers) has been referred to as one of the most versatile of systems, with real multi-purpose characteristics and able to employ a variety of different types of missiles. Its batteries are always in multiples of eight, three of which can be discounted, these being taken up by the crane.

With these it is possible to detect the presence of any type of missile, especially if the system used is a Doppler one, which only pays attention to moving objects, ignoring any which are stationary.

Mobile launchers

Anti-missile or anti-aircraft missile launchers were usually capable of being orientated in direction and elevation, with the previously aimed missiles then fired at the target. In fact, at the moment there are still many launchers with the same type of characteristic.

However, when facing a threat which materializes in a short space of time, between two and six seconds, conventional launchers do not have a great deal of purpose because they take far too long to get into position.

If a saturation attack is being dealt with, in which dozens of missiles can be involved, then the situation is even worse. There would not be enough time to reload the launchers, and as a result nothing would stop the missiles from hitting their targets. This problem is overcome with the VLS (Vertical Launch System), from which large quantities of missiles can be simultaneously fired.

SA-N-4

The picture shows two SA-N-4s manufactured in Russia along with their corresponding launcher on board the Lithuanian frigate *Aukstaitis*. This missile is 3.1m long, 0.64m wide and weighs 130kg. Its range is a maximum of 9km at a speed of more than Mach 2.

The VLS

A VLS consists of a variable number of vertical cells previously loaded with missiles of a particular type. When an attack is mounted as many missiles of the appropriate type must be fired, with firing taking place at short intervals to ensure that there are no interference problems

VERSIONS

The Standard missile is one of those with the most versions offered. Here we can see the launching of a SM-1MR from the Spanish frigate *Baleares*.

between the trajectories of one missile and another.

A VLS can be single purpose or multipurpose. In the first case only one type of missile is employed an anti-aircraft/anti-missile as a general rule, and usually the mount does not consist of a large number of cells. When dealing with multipurpose mounts such as American Mk-41, the number of cells is greater. This is because the possibility of using different types of missiles in sufficient numbers depends, to a great extent, on the total number of cells available. The Ticonderoga class vessels have two twin VLS's with 61 cells. These consist of eight Mk-41 modules with eight launchers, one of, which only contains five cells because the space for three has been taken by the crane. In the Arleigh Burke class there is one mount of 61 cells and another of 29 (four groups of eight launchers, with the crane occupying one of them).

Multiple launchers

At the moment there are also multiple mobile launchers available, this meaning that there is equipment with movement and orientation/elevation and with a number of missiles in its cells. This is the case with the Mk-49 launcher with 21 cells, which are home to

LOADING

This is the moment when a Standard ER missile is loaded into a twin launcher. To put the Standard ER missile into such a launcher it must be located in a specific, determined position, which does not allow groups of multiple firings in time periods, which are too close together.

SADRAL

The SADRAL (Système d'Auto Défense Reapprochée Antiaérien Léger), which uses the Mistral missile, is on all of the "Marine Nationale" ships as well as many foreign ones.

other short range RIM 116A RAM (Rolling Airframe Missile) anti-missile missiles.

The latest contributions to the world of multiple launchers are the Sea Ram Phalanx and the Navy Stinger.

The first consists of a Phalanx mount in which the 20mm six-barrelled Vulcan has been substituted by a launcher with eleven RAM missiles. This mount has its own monopulse Doppler radar as well as FLIR (Forward Looking Infrared).

The second has eight Stinger missiles in two housings with four launchers each. This second system relies on its own radar and tracking system. Remember that the Stinger has been a part of Navy's armament since the summer of 1983, when it was adopted to face up to terrorist attacks, although at that time in its portable version, which was fired from a gun.

Russia also has its own version of this portable anti-missile/anti-aircraft missile with the SAM-7 Grail/Strela.

SAM missiles

The acronym SAM (Surface Air Missile) encompasses all missiles used for anti-missile or anti-aircraft use. No distinctions are made

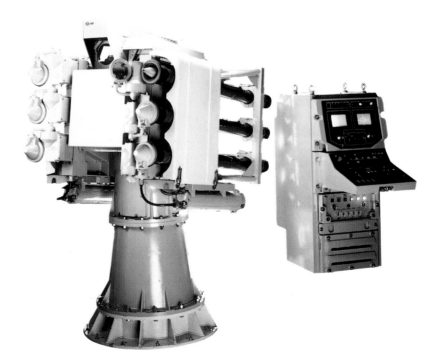

A COMPARISON OF CHARACTERISTICS

NAME/COUNTRY	SIZE	WEIGHT	RANGE (KM)	SPEED
Albatros/Italy	3.7 x 0.8	204	18.5	Mach 2,5
Crotale/France	2.9 x 0.5	85	13	Mach 2,3
Masurca/France	5.4 x 0.8	950	50	Mach 3
RAM/(USA)	2.8 x 0.4	72	9.4	Mach 2>
SA-N-6/Russia	7 x 0.9	1.500	80	Mach 6
SA-N-7/Russia	5.8 x 0.9	650	30	Mach 3
SA-N-9/Russia	3.5 x 0.5	170	12	Mach 2.5
Sea Dart/UK	4.4 x 0.9	550	65	Mach 3>
Sea Sparrow/USA	3.9 x 1	228	22,2	Mach 3>
Seawolf/UK	1.9 x 0.4	82	6.5	Mach 2>
Standard/USA	4.7 x 0.9	704	74	Mach 2> (SM-2MR)

between the models used by the ground forces or those used on board ships.

At the moment the SAM's most commonly used in Western navies are: USA, the RAM, Sea Sparrow & Standard; France, Crotale, & Masurca; Italy, Aspide; UK, Sea Dart & Sea Wolf; Russia, SA-N-1 Goa, SA-N-3 Goblet; SA-N-4 Gecko; SA-N-5 Grail; SA-N-6 Grumble; SA-N-7 Gadfly & SA-N-9.

Although these are the countries which manufacture the missiles, the number of users is much more. The use of one or the other depends on the political sphere each country belongs to. In recent years the USA has transferred a considerable quantity of ships in a reasonably up to date condition, to countries

IN-LINE MOUNTS

Not all VLS's are mounted on the deck. The Dutch Navy uses an in-line mount configuration on its Karel Doorman class frigates above the hanger port side bulkhead. This consists of 16 cells, in eight groups of two.

RUSSIAN SS-N-2 STYX

The first missile in history to sink a ship was the Russian SS-N-2 Styx. In the photograph we can see a Chinese copy of the same missile just as it is being fired from a frigate in their navy.

which in the past were politically sensitive. At the moment it is possible to find Standard missiles (SSM Harpoon as well as anti-submarine ASROC's) amongst countries which in times gone by were close to the Soviet sphere of influence. As a result of the eruption of Russian weapon manufacturers in the international

market it will not be strange to one day see Russian missiles on board the ships of countries considered to be "Western".

In addition, given that there is an active market of new ships being sold which are completely equipped as "turn-key" solutions (as was the case with the German MEKO frigates), different types of missiles may be found in the most unexpected of hands, for example Italian Aspides going to Nigeria.

Guidance systems

In general SAM missiles use guidance systems known as passive, active or active-passive, using radar, infrared or any other type of appropriate system.

In the first case, the target, an aircraft or missile, is designated by radar, with the reflected beams captured by sensitive missile sensors, which in a completely automatic way direct the missile on to the target. In the second it is the missile itself which detects the presence of a missile or aircraft to be shot down. It is often guided towards the target by using its own sensors, which can be infrared (IR) or a combination of others. The third is an ambivalent system that normally involves a first passive designation stage, then ending up in an active self-guiding mode. There are also Fire and Forget missiles, which, after firing, guide themselves straight to the target. The problem could lie in how much more it is possible to automate missiles. So many more

SEAWOLF

The Seawolf is a very precise and reliable anti-missile missile (it is said to be capable of hitting even an artillery shell) which for some time was mounted in mobile launchers. At the moment it is used in VLS's, such as those found in the type 23 or Duke class frigates of the Royal Navy.

NAVY CROTALE MOUNT

The Crotale is a light/medium type missile with great anti-missile and anti-aircraft capabilities.

countermeasure actions can be taken by using decoys. This being a more difficult situation if we are dealing with a missile guided from a ship, where there is always a human being on board who can designate another target.

However, there has always been the possibility of equipment failure or human error, as was the case with the two missiles fired form the U.S.S. *Vincennes*, which shot down an Iranian passenger airplane. Or that of the two Sea Sparrows accidentally fired from the aircraft carrier U.S.S. *Saratoga* (of the 4th fleet) on the 1st of October 1992, while carrying out NATO night time exercises and destroying the bridge of the Turkish destroyer *Muavenet*. This incident cost the lives of five people, including the ship's captain, and would have been an extremely serious incident if the missile had come from a Greek ship instead.

INDEX

New and future aircraft carriers 4

Light and medium aircraft carriers 10

Attack aircraft carriers of the US Navy 16

Lightweight squadron aircraft carriers 21

Russian aircraft carriers 26

Amphibious assault ships 32

Ballistic missile nuclear submarines 37

4th generation conventional submarines 42

Submarine weapons 48

Nuclear attack submarines 54

Present day conventional submarines 59

Modern anti-submarine warfare 64

From the Ticonderoga to the DD-21 69

Russian cruisers 75

Aegis protection 80

Modern navy propulsion systems 86

SAM missiles and their launchers 91